TOWARD THE ULTIMATE SOURCE

Planning for the Afterlife

JOZEF SIMKOVIC

To Juanzetta

This non-fiction narrative is based on many meditations, and it has been written by a former professional reporter. However, a fiction style has been used to make the story more entertaining and beneficial. It is a sequel to the *How to Kiss the Universe* book published in October 2018. Reading that book first could help you more fully understand and enjoy this story. However, it is not necessary.

While all efforts have been made not to offend any living person, the author sincerely apologizes to anyone who would be distressed or feel uncomfortable during the reading of the book. Stories and views expressed in this book have not been reviewed nor endorsed by The Monroe Institute and do not represent the policy or views of that institution (TMI).

The explanation of the terms used in the book may be found in the Updated Metaphysical Glossary at the end of the narrative.

Copyright © 2021 by Jozef Simkovic
Edited by Dr. Juanzetta Flowers
Cover Artwork by Aldren Gamalo
ISBN-13: 978-1-7325957-2-9
Library of Congress Control Number: 2021921583
How to Kiss the Universe Press, Birmingham, Alabama
Printed in the United States of America
First Edition

CONTENTS

PROLOGUE

"God made man because he loves stories." (Elie Wiesel)

The book you are holding in your hands or checking online, My Friend, can give you important benefits unlike any other you have ever read, are reading, or are planning to read. I have ventured into an ostracized area which even the most excellent writers and experts of all kinds would not dare to touch for a variety of reasons. It could jeopardize their careers, discredit their professional status, or make them the targets of mocking and jokes, including from their closest family members and best friends. I frankly do not care about such reactions at all, because as a complete spiritual being, I do not have a need to take them into account while preparing for my continued existence in the hereafter.

I simply cannot leave this planet without my message reaching as many people as it possibly can. That is why I incarnated here. I am not a famous author or public persona, and I have only you to tell others about my story if you like it. I am very thankful that you are interested.

My promises to you, Dear Reader, are based on my own experiences and the benefits I have gained from my amazing spiritual journey. You can start or facilitate your own metaphysical and spiritual journey by understanding my books and following my example.

You can get rid of all kinds of conditioning by other people, groups, and organizations which are limiting your freedom and your development as an independent powerful spiritual individual. You can connect with your deep inner self, with the consciousness existing beyond your brain and the Universe, or any other boundaries. You can connect with higher spiritual beings and get closer to the Source or God, regardless of what name you prefer and whether you believe in such an origin of your physical existence or not.

You can learn about yourself, your full history, your place and the essence and purpose on our planet and in the

Universe. You can understand that you are a timeless and unlimited being. You are limited only by the physical body you temporarily occupy. It is your vehicle, your box on this Earth, but your mind has no limits. You will understand that time and space and even universes are local.

You can get rid of your fears about what is going to happen to you after you die here on this planet. You will empower yourself better for continuing your physical life. You will feel much better about yourself. You can like people more, you can like yourself more. You can make yourself and people around you more joyful, optimistic, positive, and happy.

Before I concluded that I wanted to write a spiritual book of my own, I had read many others. I did not know that book writing was supposed to be my life mission. Many books I have read and the conversations with people who seemed to know a lot about the topic did not fully satisfy me. I decided to find out more on my own. More about how it happened is described in my first book *How to Kiss the Universe*. If you have not read that book, I strongly suggest to you, Dear Reader, that you do so. However, it is neither required nor necessary for a full understanding of this story.

Even though there are some brilliant exceptions, many authors of metaphysical and spiritual books are trying to explain simple things with unnecessarily complicated language. There are some exceptional books genuinely describing the experiences of their authors. More often, however, authors are compiling sophisticated ponderings which are sometimes difficult to understand, or they are based on the experiences of others. They might just be walking on their tip toes around a hot topic trying to be careful not to burn themselves even a little bit.

That is why I decided to figure it out on my own from ground zero all the way up to the core and purpose of our existence as humans and spiritual metaphysical beings. The subtitle of my first book was expressing that idea simply:
An Inspirational Spiritual and Metaphysical Narrative about

Human Origin, Essence and Destiny. All I need to know I learned through my dreams and by using technologically induced altered states of mind, which most people would call meditation. You can do the same, Dear Reader, whether you follow my suggestions and inspirations or find your own way.

I initiated my most profound experiences during my programs at The Monroe Institute, and in the privacy of my home, during my frequent metaphysical travels using meditation. I do not represent The Monroe Institute in any capacity and did not ask them to approve my books. I am just their client like anybody else. I am, however, an independent revolutionary spiritual explorer following in the footsteps of the great Robert Monroe while looking for the truth. Also, I am a responsible reporter sharing my real experiences with you, Dear Sister or Brother, according to the wishes of the higher beings I met in numerous spiritual realms during my travels out of body and in an altered state of mind. This book and *How to Kiss the Universe* were written neither for money nor for fame. I am living comfortably as a retired journalist and engineer for the Voice of America. I am a proud American, yet ethnic Slovak, and an introverted person speaking American English with a Central European accent. I emigrated to the United States from Czechoslovakia while it still under the communist regime.

My dearest Juanzetta, my editor and my everything, and I are not the youngest people around. We are quietly anticipating our departures from our physical lives on this beautiful planet, while enjoying our years here together. We both have had great current physical lives with their numerous successes and struggles. However, they are no more than yet another course in a school with an expected ending sooner or later. I do not call such an ending Death, but Graduation.

The dramatic and frightening happenings of 2020 and 2021 related to the Covid19 virus reminded all of us of our mortality and the fragile nature of our physical existence on this beautiful planet. This second book of mine can help you understand more about your true essence through an exciting and entertaining metaphysical narrative.

You are, my Sister or Brother, an immortal and unlimited spiritual being indeed. As such, you came into this earthly school through your temporary physical vehicle, your physical body. You will have to return to your true spiritual home sooner or later, whether you believe in it or not, and whether you want it or not. Your death will become just another graduation from this school. An understanding of this process gives you unbelievable wings of freedom, which you might be not aware of yet.

You can again be reminded from this second book of mine how you can conquer your ego and unleash your unimaginable internal powers. That can help you to become a happier and more compassionate human being for the rest of your physical life. I bet that if you are older, you are already contemplating the closeness of your graduation. If you are younger, you might be surprised how this physical life is passing quicker than you think now. You can resolve your contemplation now and stop being afraid of your graduation in the future. My books can show you how to view your limited physical life as a part of the greater universal scheme of everlasting spiritual reality, going even far beyond the time and the borders of our Universe.

What some readers apparently did not recognize and missed in my previous book, *How to Kiss the Universe*, is the fact that it talks a lot about the need to balance the feminine and masculine aspects of our lives on the planet. The building of Love, sharing, cooperation and compassion as the necessities for spiritually growing and looking for the truth winds throughout the whole book. Both books were written by a man, but with a deep respect for both genders and LGBTQ people. I am aware that spiritual and metaphysical books are read more by female readers. Ladies, please do not miss this one. And you, dear skeptic, who do not believe in any of this stuff, try to read it as a science fiction, even though it is a real story.

And everyone please, do not miss the extensive Updated Spiritual Glossary at the end of this book. It contains terms used in both books and can be extremely helpful when you are reading the stories.

Chapter 1
REUNION

"Suddenly both of our extremely high vibration forms jumped into each other like when two birds would hit each other in full flight in the middle of the air. Our forms merged in a giant flash of the light and, immediately, I saw a small dot disappearing at the speed of thought into the distance. I was slowly and calmly returning to my physical body and thinking with a little sadness:
"Goodbye Michael!"
Then remembering the Native Americans saying I corrected myself:
"Goodbye is a lie Michael because you are always with me."
(How to Kiss the Universe, Chapter 92)

Michael and I parted on June 18, 2015, as described in the quote above. For more than two years, I was fully occupied with writing *How to Kiss the Universe and* meditating only very seldom. Juanzetta and I finally went again to The Monroe Institute in October 2017 for the program, Energy Body, created and facilitated by Patty Ray Avalon. The magic of the place appeared very quickly for us and was magnified by the presence of Jerry, one of the participants. Jerry, as an intuitive psychic, during Starlines in 2010 foresaw Juanzetta and me falling in love before we even realized ourselves that it was going to happen.

While I was happy to respectfully enjoy Patty Ray's guidance in the program again, I took an individual very accelerated approach. When I woke up from a dream the first night at four o'clock in the morning, I started meditating using the Starlines II Home Exercise. After I reached Focus 42, my vibration just went crazy. Sounds of the pulsar Vela led me out of our Universe while it was also clear that Michael had sent me the dream, woken me up, and that he was around. I tried to see him and myself with the wings, but when the forms started to appear, we always merged into one. When I asked why it was happening, he said:

"You do not have to try to do that, Jozef. If you remember, we left as one as you described at the end of your book. And we are still only one because I am with you all the time. Moreover, you and I are now outside of all manifested universes. Don't you realize, that even your CHEC unit has the number one? It is not just coincidence. While there, in your unit, just feel a big empowerment and complete unity with me! Ask your questions and you shall get answers. Ask for actions and we will execute them together. Welcome back, Jozef!"

The tips of my fingers, which I placed on my heart, were extremely hot while I was unknowingly circling them around my Heartgate. With great gratitude, I was magnifying the Love streaming from the Ultimate Source through my Heartgate and sending it to everyone on the planet. I also then intuitively knew why I had ended up in the emergency room in April with swollen hands. My accumulated internal energy had been trying to be unleashed for a while and now the proper opportunity had arrived.

In Chapter 88 of my first book, *How to Kiss the Universe,* I had asked Michael, while still calling him Your Majesty, how many dimensions our Universe had. He just answered simply:

"Thirteen."

Now, after our reunion I widened that question. I wanted to know also about other universes and their dimensions. Michael said:

"You already know that there are countless universes in existence, and they each can have a different number of dimensions. When you control your mind as you do when you are coming here, you cross many dimensions without recognizing them. You do not have the tools for recognizing them. Yet that is not preventing you from reaching any space and time, and you can even peek into the Stargate as you already have."

I asked him more about the thirteen dimensions in our

Universe and he explained:

"God, the Source of Everything from your point of view, resides in your universe in dimension number thirteen. The highest three dimensions close to the Source numbered twelve, eleven and ten are non-form dimensions. They are inhabited by the highest spiritual beings just newly created by God or by those beings who are contemplating their Ultimate Graduation to return to the Source. You can call them Elohim or angels if you wish so. They do not need and do not use form-based energy vehicles while residing in their home dimension. On the other end at the lowest vibrations are your three physical dimensions. The dimensions four, five and six above your physical dimensions are the spiritual form-based dimensions. That is where your astral plane, the Belief System Territories and the Park are vibrationally located. And finally, the dimensions seven, eight and nine are transitional, or transformational and are beyond the Earth Life System. That is where the residents like to frequently experiment with their shapes, and inter-dimensional travelers are switching their non-form energy vehicles into form-based vehicles and vice versa. However, you need to know Jozef, that because I am with you, all vibrational levels are within you and easily accessible when you need to enter them."

"Does time constitute a separate dimension, Michael?"

"We do not consider time to be a dimension. However, time can be used in the higher dimensions for specific purposes. Beings living in all the universes strive for recognition and control over the dimensions they can define. You on Earth, for example, are living in three dimensions even though some believe that you are in four dimensions. Those people consider time to be another dimension. But even though you would recognize time as a dimension, you cannot move instantly in your physical vehicles into the past or the future. You can travel North and South, East, and West, you can move up and down, but you do not know how to travel back and forth in time yet. Only when you gain control of time shall you truly be living in four dimensions."

Chapter 2
LET'S TALK AND FLY!

"If you want to find the secrets of the Universe, think in terms of energy, frequency and vibration." (Nikola Tesla)

After Michael's surprising explanation, I naturally had to ask him in the next meditation:

"Hey Michael, how can I communicate with you now, when you told me you were inside of me?"

"I am inside of you all the time, but you have to always activate me, give me a signal as you just did. Just say:

"Hey Michael!" Then he continued:

"Sometimes I give you a direct answer, sometimes I give you a ROTE which you can unwind later. You must be in an altered state when you are looking for answers to complex questions. Then I can give you a ROTE. I can give you simple yes or no answers in your physical state of mind, but you still need to concentrate and be determined."

"Do I have to wait for an answer?"

"Yes, for a ROTE, no for a simple answer."

I started to tease him again about his possible incarnation on our planet. He said:

"No, I do not need and do not want to share your pains, they are parts of your experience, your earthly school. And I do not want to partake of your pleasures. You will not get me with your fried chicken!"

I understood and went back to serious questions. At first, I wanted to know about the speed of light and speed of thought. Michael explained:

"You do not have any perception of time during your spiritual travels. Your consciousness travels at the unlimited speed of thought by switching and using vibrational energy vehicles in different dimensions. The speed of light is important only when you want to move the entirety of your light or energy form vehicle to your new destination. Then you are limited by the speed of light. You can, however, use quantum entanglement   when   you want to manifest your previous physical or energy form at your destination. That way you can travel by the unlimited speed of thought. You travel as consciousness carrying only a small sample of your original energy or physical body which will be needed for manifestation at your destination. I think I already told you that, Jozef. Even your Einstein did not believe or know that it was possible. He called the instant appearing of particles at two different places a "spooky action at the distance." I use it all the time, as you know."

"Michael, you are really a spiritual genius! I am so thankful to you!"

"I am not a spiritual genius; I am just a regular angel! Can you imagine an infinite number of universes? Each of them has plenty of us. We are what you on the Earth call angels. There is so much Loosh and experiences to process for the Source. The true Heaven is where we can return if we wish to, but only if we grow enough to deserve it."

The Translucent Exercise in the Energy Body program with three messages was another good opportunity to chat with Michael. He and I were flying as one form with wings on our back in the field of the amazing bubbles of the universes. Messages were coming to us apparently directly from the Source:

Message One: A creation begins with a humming and that is the word of God.

Message Two: The word of God creates a Big Bang when the bubble of a universe is born and its strings multiply quickly like viruses or bacteria.

Message Three: A production of Loosh begins when sentient beings anywhere in the universe are created.

I took these messages as a sort of reminder because I was already aware of their content. Thus, I asked Michael to give me a ROTE about cells. It was my new interest. When he did, I started to unwind it immediately:

"Cells are elementary units of Loosh, and they do communicate. However, the real Loosh production only starts in sentient beings when the cells use higher intentions to reach an exceedingly high level of self-organization. Such a process can be very dependent on the conditions on the planet."

"Are you talking about us Earth people, Michael?"

"Yes, but on your planet also about birds and mammals. Reptiles can reach such a level too, but they ignore emotions, even when they have them. The same applies to Reptilians on other planets and moons. However, there are planets where even worms can be self-aware, as you have already experienced during your visit when Hadien took you to such a planet."

Chapter 3
ABOUT OUT OF BODY

"And you can fly high as a kite if you want to, faster than light if you want to, speeding through the Universe, thinking is the best way to travel." (Moody Blues)

The goal to get out of the body is the ultimate dream for most new spiritual explorers, but only a few of those coming to a place like The Monroe Institute seem willing to admit it openly. One of my friends is always saying:
"I just want to look down and see my body at least one time and then I will believe."

Of course, seeing your body is giving you proof of your dual essence at least. But there is much more out there than that. It took me quite a while to understand that there are as many possible interpretations for out of body experiences as the number of explorers reaching that state.

I want to advise you not to be too obsessed with a particular description from literature or any other direct or indirect source. Unfortunately, I did for a while become obsessed with the idea of having an out of body experience in a particular way. When it did not happen as I expected and hoped for, I considered it to be a failure.

The following is an illustration of such an approach and what happened to me when I tried to use The Monroe Institute's tools to get me away from my body during an exercise in the Gateway Voyage program. We had an exercise in Focus 12 with Hemi Sync support called Vibe Flow. The intention was to wiggle our astral bodies out of our physical bodies. Robert Monroe was saying on the recording:
"And now you are rolling like the log in the water!"
But I was the impatient man of the action, and I knew I was fully in an altered state, so I cockily said:
"Hey Mr. Monroe, come here please, and take me out of my body!"

Obviously, Robert Monroe, who died and moved back to the spiritual world in 1995 did not show up. I changed my tactic the next time we were again in Focus 12:

"If anybody is here, please come and pick me up out of my body!"

And there was a response. I felt at least a dozen female hands trying to lift me up, but I could also hear:

"This dude is really heavy, let's leave!"

"Would you come back, please?"

I was trying to build upon my fresh accomplishments.

"Maybe we will, but only if you are really ready."

It was too early for me to understand properly. Some of my many out of body experiences are described in *How to Kiss the Universe* book. They usually happened spontaneously in dreams, especially lucid dreams. Later, I developed better communicating skills with higher beings and I started to acquire knowledge I had never known before. Such communication is often going on without words and none of the beings have any form or bodies, including me. Thus, the question and judging of whether you are or are not out of body is truly insignificant.

There is another important point necessary to make here. Our spiritual or astral body must always be connected through a pointer to our physical body. Such a connection is usually called the Silver Cord. This cord enables us quickly to reconnect our wandering consciousness which has left our physical body. Even in the case of the strictest definition of what an out of body state is, the silver cord connecting the spiritual and physical body is always there. The part of consciousness controlling the vital physiological processes, like breathing, however, must remain in the physical body. When the Silver Cord is not there anymore, you simply are dead. People who have had near death experiences often say something like:

"I have already died three times." I say:

"I am sorry, but you did not die yet! When you are dead, you are dead, there is no way back. There is only one true total out of body experience or state, and it is called the Death. It became very fashionable in the New Age movement to talk about out of body experiences; but, sorry to say, some people often do not know what they are talking about. Sometimes, they might even exaggerate, and in rare instances, they might lie to impress their friends.

If you want to practice effective spiritual exploration, you must make sure that you are in an altered state. I am estimating that in most of my experiences, my mind is 70 to 90 percent out of my body. Not being entirely out has advantages. You need to control the necessary bodily functions, and you also need to keep a vague awareness of your surroundings, like that you are lying in a bed. The purpose of maintaining 10 to 30 percent of your mind in your brain is to enable you to follow up and execute your intention while being in an altered state; what you want to accomplish with that voyage, such as ask important questions and remember the answers. You limit yourself when you insist on travelling only when you are out of your body according to a very materialistic interpretation of such a state of mind. For example, the well-known Dr. Bruce Goldberg calls the travel that I have described here as an in-body experience. My preferable expression, even though I am not sure that I need one, would be mind of the body experience, because most of my earthly mind is out of my body.

I shall describe here an experience which happened to me much later in my spiritual journey, when I communicated with a highly developed spiritual being who calls himself Starman. I was asking him about the mind leaving the body or, as I suggested before, the mind of the body experience. Starman said:

"What is your more natural state, when you are here with us or when you are trapped in your body? You see, staying in your body is only a necessary temporary arrangement. But by leaving your physical body, you can understand who you truly are. Then, staying in your physical body can be more effective. And you can apply the knowledge you gain from here into your physical experience."

"Tell me please Starman, is it always an out of body experience when the mind is out?" I persisted.

"Yes, it is indeed. But most people believe it is out of body only when they see forms and shapes. You are already far beyond that. You do not need to have any form whatsoever to gain knowledge."

There is a lot written by many out of body explorers, for example like by my famous friend William Buhlman if you would still insist on having the so-called classical experience. He was for years a guest trainer at The Monroe Institute. I took several programs under his guidance at the beginning of my spiritual journey and learned a lot, likewise from his two classical books *Adventures Beyond the Body* and *The Secret of the Soul*.

Chapter 4
SENSITIVITY

"For a highly sensitive person, a drizzle feels like a monsoon." (Anonymous)

When you are on your spiritual way and you have raised your vibrations, you can expect that the border line between you in the physical and the beings in higher realms would not be so sharply and strictly defined. You can expect occasional breakthroughs in the membranes between our physical plane and other realms. You can detect them by all your senses.

You can occasionally see shadows, hear whisperings and other voices, smell ghosts or other creatures, you can be touched and even have strange tastes in your mouth. As an example, I woke up in January 2015 after only three hours of sleep and was walking in the hallway in a semi-hypnagogic state not quite fully awake. I heard a loud female whisper in my right ear, sure that Juanzetta was following behind me. But she was soundly sleeping in the bed. I am personally extremely sensitive to all kinds of touching by someone from the other side. I had asked Starman about that touching:

"Who is always touching me when I am waking up?"

"Usually, we are because we want you to remember your dreams. But sometimes it can be random, because as an active spiritual being you are attracting many spirits during your sleep. They are all around you and sometimes they are not careful enough. They unintentionally interfere with your astral body when you are returning to the physical body during the process of waking up."

You can also be awakened from dreams by occasional vibrations all over your body when you practice meditation and spiritual travels. That happens for two reasons. You are generally vibrating on slightly higher levels than is your normal physical state even when you are not in an altered state. Your body is much more sensitive to triggers causing vibrational changes. And, if you are waking up after only a couple of hours of sleep, the vibrations are caused by your consciousness returning to your body. You are still in a hypnagogic state and your consciousness has just jumped in or is still finishing its return to your body. Most people having out of body experiences, according to the research, vibrate shortly before leaving their body and are also still vibrating after returning to their physical body.

My sensitivity to vibrational moves and changes also showed in a little different way in a meditation in September 2010. I was practicing the slingshot technique while using the Starlines take home exercise when suddenly, during the Earth Core part of the slingshot, I had a strong feeling of a slow wobbling of the whole rather liquid core of our Mother Gaia. The liquid core was moving like a yolk would flow inside of an egg when the egg would be slowly rotated from side to side. It was remarkably interesting, yet scary.

I also had an interesting experience of sensitivity in October 2010. I had just finished my first Starlines and was looking forward to enjoying the drive home through rural Virginia. When I woke up early in the morning, I started to receive a series of words, sometimes one or two or three, and I had to take my diary to the bathroom to record them. Looking at them, I realized that they looked like possible titles of the chapters for my future book. The drive home was often interrupted by the need to stop every few miles and record a continuing stream of suggested titles into my diary. Even though I was driving very carefully, I did not pay attention to all the aspects of driving and got a speeding ticket.

Chapter 5
SEEING RAMA

"Here's to the crazy ones, the misfits, the rebels, the troublemakers, the round pegs in the square holes, the ones who see things differently, they're not fond of rules. You can quote them, disagree with them, glorify, or vilify them, but the only thing you cannot do is ignore them because they change things. They push humanity forward, and while some may see them as the crazy ones, we see genius, because the ones who are crazy enough to think that they can change the world are the ones who do." (Steve Jobs)

Naturally, the next time in the Energy Body program I met Michael again, I asked him to take us to Rama. He reacted:

"You were asking me to throw you into the Stargate for second time, remember? But you were able to do it yourself. Why don't you take us to Rama yourself?"

I directed us to the Singularity Transfer Point and then expressed the intention to see Rama. To my pleasant surprise, we flew at the speed of thought outside of our universe and I saw immediately the bubbles of universes all around us. Some of them were disappearing and others were appearing, coming out of nowhere. I realized that I was seeing the magic of bubbling in the infinity of no time.

I thought Michael would have us fly into another universe, into yet another bubble, and I asked him about that. He instead flapped our wings and started to move us majestically slowly swinging and flying between the bubbles. And then I saw Rama, outside of any manifested universe. We approached the holy cylinder, and I could see that it was constructed from beautiful light objects with shining colors.

"Is all of that pure light, Michael?" I asked in awe.

'No Jozef, it is all Super-Loosh, Super-Love. Your Rama is created from unconditional Love. That is why a Rama is outside of manifested universes. There are no Ramas in the manifested universes. The Love is compromised in manifested universes and large amounts of Super-Loosh are withdrawn from them by God. Look around, Jozef!"

Then I saw other cylinder like structures, equally beautiful, looking like our Rama. Yet, some of them had different shapes, looking like giant drops hanging in the space between the bubbles of universes.

"They are created directly by the Ultimate Creator", Michael interrupted my contemplation and continued:

"Only God can use Super-Loosh for creations of unconditional Love for housing the best servants."

I asked Michael if we could peek inside and when he allowed it, what I saw first was a young dead gorgeous Juanzetta like the one in her first wedding picture. I like to go to peek in our storage room in Alabama where she has hidden that picture. And then I saw myself, also young and handsome like in my first wedding picture.

It is hard to describe the serene and majestic beauty I saw in colors and shapes and movements I had never seen before. Golden and black sand was at the bottom of the majestic slowly rotating cylinder, and I could hear calming ocean waves and the sounds of obviously happy birds and other animals. Streams with incredibly crystal-clear waters were seen not far away flowing down the insides of the cylinder. While I was observing, Juanzetta's spiritual form walked to the still body of young man lying under the tree and entered it. The man jumped to his feet obviously happy. Then I watched my own spiritual form enter the still body of young female lying under the same tree. All the scenery was constantly changing colors. I was completely euphoric and wanted to see more, but I turned to ask Michael:

"Do you have your Rama too?"

"Of course, but my has a different name" said Michael and flapped our wings.

We were instantly at another place between bubbles, and I saw his Rama. The shape of the place was like mine and Michael let me to peek inside. Here, the shapes and colors inside were vastly different. I have never seen anything even close to it before. It seemed to me that there were many raindrop shapes inside, constantly dividing, merging appearing and disappearing. I was asking Michael if I could stay at my Rama when I heard the call to return into my physical body.

"There is your answer Jozef, you still have your physical body, and you need to leave now and go back!" said Michael.

Before the next travel to Rama, I decided to ask Michael about aether and nothing. Even though I described the morphogenetic field of dark matter and dark energy in *How to Kiss the Universe*, I wanted to have a more complete picture about everything in existence, including aether and nothing. Michael explained:

"Aether is a void, or nothing, across the unlimited all that exists. It is a void in manifested universes, and outside of them, and between them. It is outside of all that is manifested, or as you would say, digitalized or quantified. As such, aether contains dark energy, dark matter, the morphogenetic field, and space. It is not digital because it is part of the One, but unlike consciousness, it is not active. It is just there before anything manifested appears or after it ceases to exist."

I must admit it was not easy for me to digest such a short but overly complex and complicated explanation.

I impatiently waited for the next opportunity to continue in conversation with Michael about Rama's missions. And it happened during the super-flow exercise on the last day of the program. Even though the exercise was in Focus 27, I was able to raise my vibrations beyond the Earth Life System. Together with the fragment of Michael inside me, we reached the vibrational proximity of the bubbles of universes.

Rama and other similar giant spiritual ships composed of only unconditional Love appeared all around us. This time I recognized rays of concentrated lights leaving the surfaces of the giant ships and disappearing into the distance with incredible speed.

The rays just flew by us and some of them penetrated the membranes of the bubbles of universes and disappeared inside of them. I also saw rays of light going back into the ships of unconditional Love.

"What is happening here, Michael? What are those rays?" I asked him.

"The angels, as you call them, are going on their missions as you will do when you live in your Rama, Jozef."

"Are they females, or males, or both?"

"Unconditional love sent from The Source of Everything does exist in the manifested universes in a limited form. Mothers and fathers on your planet often unconditionally love their children, sometimes friends can love each other unconditionally; and even your pets might love like that. The most effective form of that love for the missions you are watching is by sending couples of lovers, usually female and male, but sometimes they can be of the same gender. They support each other tremendously, even waiting for each other when their missions in the universes are divided, because they want to come together back to the unconditional Love homes given to them by God."

Chapter 6
REMOTE VIEWING

"Facts do not cease to exist because they are ignored."
(Aldous Huxley)

My meditations with the support of Hemi Sync had brought me a lot of discoveries, knowledge, emotions, and excitement. But obviously, I was having my suspicions about how much of all that I had learned and experienced was coming from my own brain. I was looking for validation and understanding of how and where other received information was created, stored, and brought into the physical world and into my brain, and if it was objective and real.

I had been expressing my doubts very often when conferring with my guides. They suggested that I should take a course in Remote Viewing which would help me to understand the non-local nature of consciousness. I knew about such a program at The Monroe Institute, but up until the suggestion from my guides, I was never really interested in it. It had been outside of my spiritual focus.

Of course, I understand that many of you would love to learn and practice remote viewing. A top expert in the field, Paul Smith, prefers to call such abilities as Remote Perception. I fully agree with him. However, the name Remote Viewing has become more common. Remote viewing is indeed a very inviting and attractive spiritual activity. I signed up for a program led by the President of TMI at that time, Frederick Holmes (Skip) Atwater.

I took it in November 2009. When I learned to successfully describe remote objects, persons, environments, and happenings under the conditions of not knowing anything about them, I had to fully accept that the information about them was coming to me from somewhere else and not from my brain itself.

Skip gave us an excellent overview of the history of all the different kinds and methodologies of remote viewing.

We also had a dozen methodically different and precisely designed exercises. I correctly described the targets ten times out of a dozen, but in no way could I proclaim myself to be an expert whatsoever. I did not continue in the practice after the program, because I wanted to concentrate on the core of my spiritual research. But participation in the program gave me enough information to explain here very simply what remote viewing or perception is, and what it is not.

Many misconceptions and misunderstandings about Remote Viewing exist in the alternative media. Various remote viewing teachers and experts are not helping to dispel the misconceptions by shrouding the whole issue with foggy phrases when asked about it. Sometimes I think that they are doing that simply to keep the secrets of the trade intact.

First and foremost, remote viewing is not qualified or non-qualified guessing about remote non-local objects, people, environments, or happenings. When someone not trained in remote viewing just closes his or her eyes, or even goes into an altered state and is trying to see the target, that is not remote viewing. He or she is just trying to use his or her psychic abilities to picture a remote target in the brain without a formalized procedure or protocol. This is just pure psychic intuitive guessing or even speculation, nothing more.

Remote viewing is a specific activity based on a protocol. The protocol is necessary to minimize the influence of subjective personal guessing or wishful thinking. The creators and organizers of the famous secret military Stargate program understood that this must be done from the beginning of the training of potential remote viewers and continue all the way up to practical applications.

Remote Viewing is a specific psychic activity that requires talent, but more than anything else, hard work. Anybody can try. As a top remote viewer Joe McMoneagle says, we all are psychics. I would add that anybody can try to play the violin or ice hockey, and many successfully do, but only a few can become as successful as David Oistrakh or Wayne Gretzky. The most important part of the training is the monitoring of the viewer by the objective judging of his or her final description of the target.

A remote viewer relaxes and eventually goes into an altered state; then she or he connects to a target and collects its fragments one by one. She or he is connecting and disconnecting from a target usually in fractions of a second and is doing it many times while trying not to put any subjective suggestions and opinions into the process.

Thus, the result of the viewing is composed of numerous bites of consciousness into the target. She or he is trying to keep them as short as possible, even shorter than a blink of an eye. The viewer is attempting to eliminate subjective suggestions, interpretations, conclusions or even speculations. When she or he catches herself or himself doing that, such a fragment is disregarded as a so-called analytic overlay.

It is the misunderstanding of this process that creates the illusion that a remote viewer sees a remote target. The viewer is a composer only, not a seer. A top remote viewer composes images of parts of the target from numerous downloads delivered from the target into his brain with incredible speed. It just seems that image of the target is coming momentarily into his or her mind. It is a similar process to how an analog TV picture is created. You just see the picture, but not the beam in the tube. Bites can be recognized in the brain by all five senses, or even by Extra Sensory Perception (ESP).

Different remote viewing schools have different protocols. There is also a need to eliminate the so-called Front Loading even before connecting to the target. That was the second most important thing I learned at the program and incorporated into my metaphysical travels. You must recognize and eliminate your wishful thinking before getting fully engaged in a spiritual conversation in an altered state. Front Loading elimination fully applies in both remote viewing and metaphysical travel. Otherwise, you can get messages tainted by unwanted information from your physical memories.

The first connection to a target is through the basic structure or skeleton, which is usually called the Gestalt. A viewer then proceeds from that gestalt all way to, at times, very amazing details. For example, when I was viewing a target in one of our exercises, I had the feeling from the beginning that it was a house. But I had to fully disregard that feeling as analytic overlay and apply the protocol, during which I composed the object from numerous connections to the target. It turned out to be a house on the Icelandic coast anyway. During short downloads, I had even received the smell of cooking. Yet it was clear to me, that by proclaiming it was a house at the beginning, I could be tricked into it by my physical brain. A house would be very general, but a house on the Icelandic coast is more specific.

Sometimes people, without understanding how remote viewing really works, might ask a rather naive question like:
"Can I remote view this or that?"
It is similar question like someone without musical experience and skills would ask:
"Can I take a violin and play a symphony?"
I would answer:
"Yes, of course, you can. Anybody can, but first you have to learn how to play the violin and then you can work your way up to a symphony."
It is same with the remote viewing. You must learn the protocol and tools and then practice a lot first. I hope you understand my point.

It is not my intention here to talk too much about remote viewing. I just hope that this chapter can help you take another look at what remote viewing really is and eventually find a good teacher if you are interested.

Chapter 7
HEALING

"In order to see, we must first become blind to all that we know." (Paul Rademacher)

In one of the first exercises in the Energy Body program, Michael explained to me what he described as a Kundalini Loop. It is a continuous flow of godly energy from the Source and back, through all the human chakras in both directions. It can be intensified by the Universe's energy entering the crown chakra and by Mother Gaia's energy entering the ground chakra. We can likewise release our magnified positive energy into the Universe or Earth Core. The loop can oscillate in waves, becoming smaller or bigger depending on our communication influencing energy. Being able to manipulate the Kundalini Loop enables us to create and use energy vehicles and connections across dimensions, time, space, and universes.

I became immediately aware of a little blockage in my third chakra after having had little issues with my throat for several months. After clearing the blockage, I started to feel better. One of the Energy Body program exercises then became very handy. We visited the Healing and Rejuvenation Center in Focus 27 where the Park is vibrationally located. I asked for healing tailored to my little health problems.

My friends in the center first put my spiritual body with the form of my physical body in a cylinder which started to rotate around me. They told me my chakras needed a small adjustment. The colors of the chakras were fuzzy at the beginning, but during the rotation of the device my chakras became very sharp and rotated into the shapes of discs. When the device slowed down, the chakras returned to their natural cone shapes. The heart chakra, my Heartgate, had two intertwined flickering colors of green and pink.

The chakra balancing was followed by several other

treatments. They put me into what they called an Anti-allergy egg. A series of little lighting like sparks from the shell of the unit hit me all over my spiritual body and I felt a slight itching all over my physical body. My spiritual body in the egg seemed to have fur like a dog or cat. Siphons from the shell sucked the fur away from my body, and afterwards I saw and felt little injections all over my body.

I also received a thyroid gland boost. Light impulses targeted my third chakra. After that, something like a brush went through my mouth all the way down to my stomach and back, obviously helping me with my acid reflux. Because I play a lot of table tennis, I asked for a balancing of the moving parts of my body. Another spiritual device was circling around my main joints to stimulate them, especially the right hip, lower back, and right elbow. I felt tremendous relief and relaxation after receiving the healing I had asked for.

I would like to say here, Dear Reader, that if you think all of this is just spiritual quackery, I have no physical proof for you that these processes work. I can only tell you my experiences and feelings. For example, one of them was the rejuvenation of my heart after I discovered and activated my Heartgate, as described in *How to Kiss the Universe*. Even though I do not often practice the specific targeted healings as described here, I feel refreshed and rejuvenated after every meditation. That is true even when I do not have any specific messages or other intended or expected results of the meditation. The mainstream media will describe the benefits of meditation only in so-called scientific, but very vague and foggy language. It seems that going into a deeper understanding of the supremacy of mind over matter and energy is still a social taboo.

Chapter 8
CHRISTMAS EVE

"For those who would die, there is life. For those who would dream, there is reality. For those who would hope, there is knowledge. For those who would grow, there is eternity."
(Robert Monroe, Far Journeys)

For me as a Central European originally from Slovakia, Christmas Eve is the biggest holiday of the year. For Central Europeans it is sort of a combination of Christmas and Thanksgiving Day. Families meet, exchange gifts, and express their gratitude to God and celebrate the birth of Jesus Christ. Kids are told that the gifts were brought by Baby Jesus, instead of by Santa Claus like in America, or by Grandpa Frost in Russia.

After Juanzetta accepted the customs from my former Motherland, we had a wonderful Christmas Eve 2017. Afterwards, while fully relaxed and happy, I felt the strong urge to meditate. The Energy Body program was still fresh in my memory, and I opted for the Home CD from that program because it is dedicated to gratitude. I wanted to reinforce my experiences from the Energy Body program without any specific intention. I felt that I should go in my altered state to the Nancy Penn Center.

I have not been at the Nancy Penn Center for a while, and I needed some time to find the stairway down to the Fox Den. When I did, I sat there for a while and then decided to go over to the administration building, David Francis Hall. However, when I was about to open the Fox Den's outside door, it opened toward me, seemingly by itself, and a young-looking Robert Monroe walked in! I was in a shock and let him know that. Again, as had happened often before when you expect the least you get the most. He pointed to the couch next to the door and we sat down. Still in a state of shock, nothing was coming into my mind; thus, I tried to tell him about my book.

After listening to my rather chaotic explanation, he looked at me with deep kindness displayed in his face and said:

"I know your script, Jozef."

I was shocked that he knew my name. He continued:

"Do not be surprised Jozef. I can see your writings from the spiritual realm. By the way, thank you that you dedicated your first book to me. Also, thanks for explaining my discoveries in simple terms, and even better than I did. You know things like Loosh, ROTE, focus levels, lower astral ring, BSTs and all the rest. I could not do it in my time in plain language. I had to be much more careful and had to mystify my experiences since there were many bigoted people all around us. The circumstances were not as easy and relaxed in seventies and eighties as they are now here on Earth."

Then he quickly changed the topic and told me:

"I am coming here every Christmas Eve. It is the quietest evening here for me in the whole earthly year and the most sacred. I usually become very sentimental. I will be sentimental again after you leave, Jozef. I know your time here is limited, so would you like to ask me something?"

I was still in awe and could not find my words, so I just thanked him for all I had learned from him and asked him if he possibly knew my friend Michael:

"Of course, Michael and I are friends. I am busy not only with trying to influence the minds of those leading my institute on the Earth, but I am also helping in other star systems."

Then I asked him if he had message for his Monroe Institute and he answered:

"Yes, I do. It is time for them to get out of the diapers, so to speak. They need to be more specific about all in our system as I designed and developed it. They must go deeper and deeper into my books and now also into your book. They also need to widen their public relations activities. They need to penetrate into all kinds of mainstream media." And he continued:

"Remind them that they are now in the 21-st century. The time has arrived to get out of the vegetative non-profit status and start to build a foundation for the university as you envisioned it in your book. That vision should be taken seriously. I gave that message to you because I saw that you were more perceptive about the big picture then the leadership of the institute was."

Patty's voice in my headphones called me back to C1 and into my physical body. I quickly expressed boundless gratitude to Robert and flew back home to my dear Alabama.

Chapter 9
TEN METAPHYSICAL COMMANDMENTS

"Thy eyes shall see what no one saw yet." (Message to the Author from the Universe on January 8, 2010)

On April 18, 2018, while relaxing in the kitchen in Juanzetta's condo in Birmingham, without any intention or asking, I received an amazing ROTE of Ten Metaphysical Commandments. I must have unknowingly shifted into an altered state. Here is the unwound content:

1. You are more than your physical body.

2. There is no beginning and no end, there is only motion.

3. There are an infinite number of universes manifested from the stillness by the bubbling of the Ultimate Creator, who is the Source of Everything.

4. Time and space in the manifested universes are only local and temporary.

5. You came into the spiritual existence by separating from the Ultimate Creator and you can completely return to the Source if you want to.

6. You are a powerful and immortal spiritual being.

7. God as The Source of Everything is ever present in you and in All That Exists.

8. You have the free will to be able to choose your spiritual path and destiny.

9. You can strengthen your essence and destiny by absorbing, accepting, magnifying, and spreading the unconditional Love

given to you by the Ultimate Creator.

10. You can have an instant communication in metaphysical realms by utilizing the ball of information known as Related Organized Thought Energy (ROTE).

Chapter 10
INTRUDERS

"When you love your enemies, you have no enemies."
(Lisette Larkins, Talking to ETs, page 139)

At the end of April 2018, Juanzetta and I were going to The Monroe Institute for the Starlines Reunion program. Four days before the program I dreamed that Juanzetta and I were at The Monroe Institute in a room with tables and chairs. We were sitting in the last row, but the rest of the group was having a discussion on the other side of the room. Trainer Andrea walked over to us apparently to ask us why we were not with the rest of the group, but I interrupted her by telling her that I needed to give her a hug. Then I woke up.

The Starlines Reunion was led by its creator Dr. Franceen King. The second trainer was Andrea Berger. Franceen received the guidance in May 2016 to create a program with the main goal of trying to initiate physical contact with extra-terrestrials or extra-dimensionals. She did not want to call such beings aliens as she had had a personal experience with a spacecraft in the 1970s north of Bethesda in Maryland. Our group was only the third group to take this program.

Before Franceen's presentation on the first full day on Sunday had begun, I had to deal with a rather unusual and unpleasant situation also affecting some other participants in the group. The first exercise on Saturday evening was a reset of Focus 27. I had only one channel working in my headphones. That is rare, since the equipment at The Monroe Institute is always reliable. I felt, however that Michael was aware of it and had sent some spiritual helpers who balanced my spiritual body, and I was able to reach Focus 27. Yet, I heard not only Michael, but also Robert Monroe lamenting about my state.

At 1:45 am, I had a dream of being at The Monroe

Institute in a high-rise building where someone was trying to get inside of our room through the window. I was screaming in my dream in Slovak four times:

" Pomoc, pomoc, pomoc, pomoc! (Help, help, help, help!)" Juanzetta had to wake me up. It was obvious that some malevolent spiritual entity tried to enter our space to disrupt our group. Windows in a dream usually represent portals and the high building obviously represented our high vibrations as a group. Everybody had already taken both Starlines programs, the top TMI courses.

Several other group members were fully aware of this attack. Stig, our friend from Norway, was sleeping in the next room. He told us that he not only heard my screams but felt a lot of negative energy around. Howard thought that a bad entity ended up in his room because he dreamed about windows and people bothering him inside, too. John had a Near Death Experience. Carlie reminded us that we spiritually perceive more in the night because we are less egocentric and more open. Franceen tried to calm us down by expressing the usual favorite trainers' opinion about this type of situation by saying that we should consider it to be our own mis-creations, our own constructs.

I chose to include this story here because it shows that negative forces can try to infiltrate into even powerful sophisticated meditative groups, as our Starline Reunion friends and trainers were. I decided to take the first opportunity to deal with the situation, especially when Juanzetta told me that, for the first time ever, she met with my guides that Sunday morning.

I was determined to catch any intruder and put him or her into my Energy Conversion Box. The creature I grabbed looked like a giant sponge box with sides about one foot long. When I tried to put the entity into the box, it produced squeaky sounds and tried to stick itself to my legs with its tiny like octopus' arms. I struggled but finally was able to force it into the box. The resilient creature lifted the cover several times by pushing it up from inside the box, but I was able to close and lock it for good.

Then I met Michael in Focus 34/35. He said: "You seem to be getting better."

I told him what happened. He warned me that there were a bunch of these creatures around. He gave me a bag and suggested:

"Take this bag and put all of them in it. They are in Howard's room and all-around the Nancy Penn Center. You must fight tricksters with tricks. Just tell them that you are holding their buddy and promise to release them all if they jump into the bag. Then make your Energy Conversion box bigger and toss the bag into it. They will not bother anybody in your group anymore."

"But who are they anyway, Michael?"

"Spiritual viruses, cosmic garbage; they are not part of the Divine Structure of Consciousness. Remember how they like to hang around the Stargate?"

I did as Michael told me and promised to release them when I got back home from TMI. I somehow felt sorry for them and told them that I loved them anyway. Then I fully opened my Heartgate and received an extra high dose of Love directly from the Ultimate Creator, not only for me but for the whole group. I was confident that an attack on our group would not happen again, and it did not.

A little different personal spiritual assault happened to me about four months later. Juanzetta and I were driving toward Quebec City after the trip around the lovely Gaspe peninsula. We stopped on the bank of the Saint Lawrence River near the town of Levis to see several large sand statues. It was nice artwork. One of them was a statue of Baphomet, a pagan or gnostic idol or deity that the Knight Templars were accused of worshipping. It was very well done, and I stood looking at it for a while.

When we came to our room 222 at Auberge Saint Antoine in the heart of Quebec City, I found a small magnifying mirror in the bathroom. Before realizing the mirror was a trap, I stunk my tongue out, my eyes went bug-eyed starring into the mirror, and I saw my face changing into the face of Baphomet. I felt a strong pull into the mirror. I heard in my mind:

"See, I am here, you just must connect with me more and I can teach you a lot."

Stupid, aggressive thoughts and suggestions entered my mind, and I realized the danger. I had to avoid that mirror as much as possible during our whole otherwise joyful, wonderful stay in that room. I had voluntarily stepped into that creature's wisely set up trap.

The well-known investigative mythologist William Henry supports a possibility of connecting with guides and deities by concentratedly staring into their pictures. That had happened to me even without my conscious intention to do it. The malevolent entities do not need much leeway to be invited into your psyche.

Chapter 11
ULTIMATE HIGHER SELF

"You'll never rise any higher than the way you see yourself." (Joel Osteen)

Starlines Reunion, after eliminating intruders and clearing any of the negative energy left, continued at full steam. Franceen presented many possible reasons why ETs do exist, like ancient texts, creation stories, suggestive ruins, statistical probabilities, and reports from contact experiencers, meditators, channelers and others. We set our minds on the possibility of meeting Greys, human looking ETs, Reptilians, insectoids, hybrids, and others. We talked about a variety of suggested protocols for contacts and created teams for projecting and creating landing maps and directions for any eventual visits.

I was genuinely surprised that the emphasis was put on trying to make physical contact, which could be difficult to attain and prove; and such expectations could lead to big disappointments. When we signed up for the program, I thought it would be more oriented toward communications at even higher vibrational frequencies than both previous Starlines programs. Thus, I decided like before, while fully respecting the flow of the program, to use my own individual approach and intentions. The first opportunity arose in the exercise Self Review, which used the energies of the vibrational space of Focus 34/35.

After getting into Focus 34/35, I immediately discovered my very own Divine Structure of Consciousness. I have 175 I-There Clusters and 25 Higher-Higher Selves in different galaxies, dimensions, parallel universes, and multiverses. The connection from my current physical incarnation on the Earth vibrationally all way up to the Ultimate Higher Self was truly clear, suggestive, teasing and inviting. I could also identify and research other connections from my Ultimate Higher Self all way down to some of my other I-There clusters if I would be interested in doing that. But for the time being I was not. I also did not detect any current existing connections from other I-There Clusters to any physical planets. I realized that it meant that I did not have any other concurring physical incarnations elsewhere. That meant I could raise my spiritual vibrations directly from the Earth to my Ultimate Higher Self, bypassing the BSTs, the Park, and all other dimensions and go directly to the 12th dimension after I died on the Earth.

I understood that if I would do that, I could then choose to rejoin the Ultimate Creator in dimension 13 or decide to stay at Rama, which is in the 12th dimension. From Rama, I could use my essence composed of unconditional Love to travel as an Ambassador of Love, angel, or spiritual missionary into the lower vibrational areas anywhere in the manifested universes. I understood that settling into any lower vibrational dimensional level would mean to be stuck again and be looped into the chains of multiple reincarnations in that dimension. They could be interesting, even pleasurable, but as we on our planet know well, it could also be full of pain, suffering, disappointment, sorrow, and many other struggles. I am not for that anymore. I have learned my lessons and I know that I am an Ultimate Graduate in waiting.

I still, however, must continue in a variety of ways to help people on this planet for the remainder of my physical life here. That is why I have written this second book to try to help anybody willing to understand the bigger picture of our being here. I am a very emphatic person and often take on the physical pains of people close to me, like Juanzetta, both of my sons, my brothers, great nephews and even people I barely know. One thing I know for sure, that after my physical death here, I need to secure my bliss and vibrate directly to my Ultimate Higher Self. That will be my major award for my spiritual mission on this planet.

Chapter 12
PONDERING

"A man who has no imagination has no wings." (Muhammad Ali)

On Monday evening, the group broadcasted our first invitation to the ETs by using the Earth Core floating energy. It was also preparation for our field trip the next day into the Luray Caverns, where we would do resonant tuning as a group. The afternoon exercise was dedicated to the Portal Room where one can set up a visit into any other time and space.

I had a lot of questions for Michael. I learned from him that the Higher-Higher Self can attract and absorb the lower selves and take them vibrationally higher toward the Source. You must attract all aspects and fragments of your vibrational downline structure, without any residuals, on your final journey after departing from your physical body. That way you can become an Ultimate Graduate. You can then reside in the 12th dimension and directly communicate with God.

I call all this the Ultimate Choice. The choice is simple for me, either go back to my true home, the True Heaven, and complete unity with the Ultimate Creator, or choose to continue my spiritual existence as an Ambassador of Love residing in the place of unlimited Love. One of those places is our Rama. If you wish to do this, Dear Reader, you must first spiritually grow into such a position. If you want to leave our Earth Life System, you must have the spiritual velocity to be able to do so. If you want to consciously plan your next reincarnation on our planet, then you go to a place like the Park. If you believe what your religion or other beliefs are telling you and you want to meet your people again, you might want to go to your Belief System Territory. From there, you can incarnate back and forth as much as you like. If you do not believe in anything like that, you might just get lost in a lower astral plane like Focus 23, recycling back and forth to Earth even without knowing what is going on.

If you reach the state of knowing as I have and you are vibrationally able to reach the Stargate, you should think twice about what you want to do and then be confident and determined to execute your decision. However, you might not be able to come back to a materialized universe after you have entered the Stargate. I was able to do it twice, but only because my dear teacher and friend Michael warned me, and I spent only a short time there. Michael himself made his own very firm decision to stay in the top dimensions of the manifested universes. According to what he said, he was not trying to go to the Source anymore. He wanted to continue the work he was doing.

If you want to reach the point of the Ultimate Choice, however, you must be able to build your vibrational skills and obtain a Light Body. Then, the transfiguration of your physical body into the Light Body will be instantaneous after your final departure from the physical environment. You will then appear in the 12th dimension as an energy body without any form and you can touch and kiss the Ultimate Membrane, the Skin of God, as many times as you want.

Juanzetta and I participated in the Convergence Conference in Nashville in April 2018 which was led by the investigative mythologist William Henry and his wife Clare. Henry has dedicated a lot of his time to explaining the different ways of how to reach a Light Body state, as well as the Ascension to the Ultimate Source. I wanted to know what he would do after accomplishing the Ascension, so I asked him. He was apparently a little surprised by my question but answered anyway:

"I guess I just want to be a janitor around God's Throne."

At that time, I was surprised by his answer and not fully satisfied. But I must say that I fully understand now. What he said is just a different version of what I described two paragraphs above.

Chapter 13
AMBASSADORS

"The key to interstellar travel lies in mastering the creative process, not in acts of technological conquest." (Diana Luppi aka Zoev Jho, E.T.101)

Franceen was profoundly serious about our Starlines Reunion group acting as galactic ambassadors. One of the participants even created and brought for each one of us beautiful pins which proclaimed us Galactic Ambassadors of Starlines Voyager 8. They were to remind us of our mission during the program.

It was our second meditation of the day, and it was Wednesday. In every program I attended at The Monroe Institute, the broad-band flow of information in multiple ROTEs and exciting and revealing experiences start to ramp up on Wednesday. Some female participants can secretly even admit to having orgasms during meditations in the CHEC units on Monroe Wednesdays. I must admit being awfully close to having one, too, several times, even though having a spontaneous orgasm is not as easy for men as for women.

The guided meditation led us into the auditorium at the Alpha X Station. It is a huge round room with a glass roof enabling one to see many stars, galaxies, and nebulas. When I got there, the room was already full of representatives of all the possible races and species from our Galaxy. It was a session of the Council of Galactic Guardians. I could see people just like us, Greys, tall blond ones, Reptilians, praying mantises, people in fur coats, jellyfish-like beings, and other forms of sentient beings too difficult to describe. There was a round table in the middle of the room with about fifteen armchairs already occupied with a variety of these beings. Only one armchair was empty. The auditorium was full without any empty seats.

Suddenly, everybody in the hall stood up like one as

Michael came into the room dressed in a full white robe. He raised his hands, which changed into wings. He flapped the wings toward the table and several times toward the audience before he sat down in the chairman's armchair. Then he presented the agenda for the two parts of the meeting. The first part was dedicated to reports about Loosh production in languages I did not understand. I just caught that he reprimanded the Reptilians about their slow and low production.

The second part of the proceedings was dedicated to the planet Earth, whose representatives had invited the participants into their spiritual space station. Michael said:
"Thank you for inviting us all to this beautiful Space X Station. I personally thank the leader of the planet Earth group from the planet's leading spiritual institution, The Monroe Institute. I also thank Dr. Franceen King for her efforts to reach us and every citizen of our Galaxy. That institute is leading in the efforts to stop and reverse negative developments on their planet. We all here are very aware of the rising hate there, the humans' fears on the planet and the growing uncontrollable greed. The only way for the people on the planet to move themselves in the right direction is for them to recognize their true spiritual essence. That could lead to increasing the production of good quality Loosh, which is necessary for our mutually beneficial relationship to the Ultimate Creator. We can see some good pockets actually increasing the Loosh production, but the planet is still on a slippery slope and that is dangerous."
Michael paused and tremendous applause from the participants followed. Then he continued:
"I also welcome Franceen's assistant Andrea and the sixteen members of the Earth delegation. I would like to recognize Jozef Menev Skjoerg Plautus who has the great potential to contribute to the increase of spiritual awareness on the planet, even though it has not fully materialized yet. I am glad that he wrote his book, and he told me he would like to write another one. I want you to know that he is also my friend and

I like to spend some time with him in one of my spiritual identities whenever he is available and out of his physical body. He has already done what I asked him to do, and I have no doubts that he shall continue to do more until the earthly day of his departure to his real spiritual home near and around our dear Ultimate Creator."

The call in the headphones came to return to TMI. Michael was about to close the meeting anyway and we waved goodbye to each other. Back in the white carpet room in the Nancy Penn Center after the exercise, participant Dan told me that he saw me at some meeting and that I had a special role in it.

Chapter 14
AMAZING JESHUA

"Many are standing before the door, but it is the solitary ones who will enter the wedding hall." (The Gospel of Thomas, Saying 75)

I met Michael again in the next Wednesday morning exercise and thanked him for the recognition at the meeting of the Council of Galactic Guardians. He said he had no more to tell me about the Stargate and the Ultimate Choice. But, if I would like he could tell me more about Rama, because he lived in a Rama himself. He said he could also arrange a meeting with Jesus Christ for me and I could ask him whatever I would like. I was incredibly happy, and he did that.

Jesus (Jeshua) came in a similar white robe to what Michael wore at the meeting of the Council of Galactic Guardians. I asked Jeshua if I could go into Stargate again. He said he would not recommend it now, especially if I would like to keep my spiritual existence after I expired in my physical body on Earth. He said I could decide then what to do. I was very curious and asked him about his Second Coming to our planet. Jeshua answered:

"I have embodied many times on many different planets in many different universes to see directly how sentient beings were enjoying their physical bodies and to see their struggles. But I very rarely have experienced such cruelty or seen so much hate, greed, and fear as on your planet. I had enough and decided to leave your planet. I looked around your world and could not take it anymore. I decided to take the first opportunity to quit. And then, I experienced my own fear with an incredible intensity while being crucified. Right now, I do not want to come there again and walk amongst you people on Earth. I will only come for the second time to annihilate your planet, when you have reached the point of no return. Then every living creature would have to find their spiritual return to my Father and Mother entirely on their own. It is possible that you Earth people might wake up and start to love each other and other creatures, and then I can come for the second time. I can teach and show your people the way to grow and get close to your Stargates. Yet, I am very skeptical regarding your abilities to change. Your religious organizations and sects categorize and mark souls as good or bad in relation to their own criteria. They are also claiming that I came to your planet to take all your sins on myself, and because of that, to let myself suffer so much to save you. And that is nonsense. Yes, I came to save you, because you were becoming more and more barbaric like the most vicious animals. I came to save you by showing you another way, to change, to become better and to put more Love into your lives. It did help you not to become completely self-destructive.   It worked for more than two thousand years, but you are getting back into your selfish, greedy, and hateful ways. First, your people must find the way to remove all divisions between themselves or confirm that they are unable to do so. Then I can come again. This situation is currently not solved. There is no middle way, Jozef Menev Skjoerg Plautus!" And Jesus Christ left.

The next exercise started in the afternoon, and I knew it would be great because it was Wednesday. I was impatient to cross through the Stargate again despite warnings from both Michael and Jesus. Extremely high vibrations had already overtaken me during the resonant tuning. After I reached Focus 15, I decided to use the Singularity Transfer Point and slingshot myself directly to the Stargate. I was clearly seeing an aperture in the membrane with the edge of the Stargate gently bubbling.

I had no type of form; I was an elastic cloud of energy having nothing else but small lips coming out of it. Before going in, I decided to kiss the Ultimate Membrane several times all around the Stargate. I was kissing the Skin of God again and again. Why not? A kiss is the expression of Love for us humans. I also was expressing my Love to Jesus by thinking about the Christian cross in my mind. Then I retrieved and activated my Super-Loosh heart in my mind. With this support, I positioned myself in the middle of the Stargate and sneaked into the Source like an octopus would by using my elongated cloud-like shape.

A giant flash of light blinded my spiritual perception of seeing. I saw Jeshua in front of me in his all-body white robe. Then my elongated cloud form changed into vertical, and I was standing with Jesus on a platform in the bottom of the bubble around us.

"I am humbled, My Lord, to see you. I love you with all of my heart and mind and I brought you a gift!" said I.

Then I stretched out both my hands holding my Super-Loosh heart, offering it to him. He answered:

"I know who you are, Jozef. You have the same name as my earthly father had. I have been following your earthly life since your childhood when I was giving you signs in dreams. I sometimes moved my eyes on the cross in your room in Láb. The last time I moved my eyes and fingers for you was in Nashville when William Henry was showing the copy of painting of me called "Salvator Mundi" by Leonardo da Vinci. You can keep your Super-Loosh heart, Jozef. It can now multiply itself as many times as you wish to give it away. I know you understand, but I still must emphasize that you cannot trade it for anything. You can only give it away when you are spreading my Love around. Look around you. As far as you can see are My Father and My Mother, their Holy Spirits and their Love."

I looked around but I could not see beyond the clear glass-like crust of the bubble. I saw only the bubbling of the Ultimate Membrane which would occasionally pop out and suck the bottom of the bubble. I did not admit to seeing anything beyond the clear crust and Jeshua said:

"Jozef, before you leave, I have to show you who I also really am."

I looked at him and his form changed to Buddha, then Melchizedek, Abraham, Mohamed, Krishna, Shiva, Manitou,

Zoroaster, and many other spiritual leaders from Earth that I could not recognize. The changing of the shapes was very quick, and I was in instant bliss.

"I cannot keep you here for long because you still have your physical body on Earth. You have to go now," said Jeshua.

"Thank you, my Lord, I did not deserve this blissful moment!" said I.

And Christ answered:

"Yes, you did, Jozef. Your Love and your dedication to your sisters and brothers and all living beings brought you here."

A big flash of light followed, and I was outside of the membrane kissing it again. The Stargate disappeared.

Earthly time went by, and Jesus remembered me again. I received a ROTE directly from him while in my physical body in early December of 2018. I was incredibly surprised because Michael had told me that I had to come for a ROTE in an altered state. Jesus sent me the following message in the rote:

"Incarnation is hard work, Jozef. You will be in danger of incarnating again if you decide to reside in the place of unconditional Love which you call Rama. You will hear suffering sentient beings on or inside of the physical planets and moons calling for help. That can overcome you, because you would be composed of only unconditional Love as an angel or Elohim. Your unconditional Love and compassion for such beings can lead you to senseless suffering, as it happened to me on Earth, because you will not be thinking about yourself. If you are not ready for that again, return to your true home, to my Father as I used to say on your planet Jozef. Go back directly through the Stargate into the Source where you came from into your spiritual existence. However, you must know that there is no way back into a spiritual existence as the same being. My bubble you visited is protecting me only temporarily. You can also try to go into the Source temporarily, but I cannot help you to come back. Your choice is simple, to be an Elohim or not to be an Elohim."

Chapter 15
CHUNK

"Reincarnation occurs because we decide that we haven't learned enough lessons." (Sylvia Browne)

Almost every evening of the program we had wonderful ET inviting group sessions under the stars on the beautiful meadow of The Monroe Institute. The institute is in rural Virginia in the mountains and there is extraordinarily little ambient light. The goal of the group was to contact biological ETs. We were following Franceen's elaborate strategy and guidance and singing together the wonderful Kumbaya (Come by Here). We were excited and our expectations and feelings were good, even though we received no direct physical proof of contact. It was obvious that ETs were around us and it was much like it happened during Starlines I in 2010, when Juanzetta and I met for the first time. I described it in *How to Kiss the Universe* in Chapter 41. Like at that time, some participants like John, Dan, Virginia, Susan, Franceen and Andrea saw small glimpses of brown discs.

Thursday was the last day of the program and I knew I would have several amazing experiences. The first opportunity arrived with an exercise in the Light Spa with the Subatomic Accelerator. The powerful Palenque sounds were bringing something very substantive with a lot of energy from all parts and corners of the Universe into my body early in the exercise. My body was fortified with huge amounts of energy and felt ready to burst at any moment. My Light Body missile was getting ready for a launch.

I suddenly understood. I was pulling all my other 174 I-There Clusters (Higher Selves), with all their experiences and Loosh, and my 24 other Higher-Higher Selves into my Ultimate Higher Self. The pilot light of my base chakra burst into an incredible ball of light, and I was in front of the Stargate. I had reached the Totality of Self with only one clear connection in the manifested universes remaining. Except for that connection, I had integrated all my metaphysical structure into one point. The only remaining connection was in our Universe from my Ultimate Higher Self in the 12th Dimension all the way vibrationally down through the remaining Higher-Higher Selves from the 11th Dimension to the 5th Dimension, and through my Earth's I-There Cluster (Higher Self) in the 4th dimension to my three-dimensional physical body on the Earth.

That was more than enough. Happy and satisfied with my accomplishment, I decided to join the exercise again by going directly into the Light Spa. I quickly realized that I was very well ahead of the guidance in the exercise. All that the guidance voice was telling me to do, I had already done. However, I knew there was still something I needed to do.

My Light Body appeared in the middle of the Light Spa. Colorful rays of light were coming from the wall and fortifying and purifying my Light Body more and more. Then I realized that those light rays were coming from outside of the spa, penetrating its walls and entering my Light Body. I recognized that I was pulling in the bonds with the I-There Clusters of all the spiritual beings I was connected to in my entire spiritual existence. I was becoming a Chunk of the Infinite Sea of Bonded I-There Clusters. The great Robert Monroe was the one who discovered and observed their existence and occasional disappearing. I had become complete spiritual being who was able to gather my own chunk. It is obvious that I could now disappear into the Source and have everlasting unity with the loving God if I choose to do so. I could also choose to stay in the place of unconditional Love, which Juanzetta and I call Rama.

Michael reminded me more about the Elohim almost one year later in my meditation:

"Elohim like me, and like you in your spiritual future, Jozef, are the complete spiritual beings residing in the 12th dimension of your universe or completely outside of your universe. They have either just separated from the Source or are ready to return to God after fully completing their spiritual missions. They can choose to go back into the Ultimate Creator, the Source of Everything. Unlike you, Jozef, I do not want to go back yet as you know. If you would try to lure me to go back to the Source through the Stargate, I would step out of your Elohim vehicle. I am not going to join you, but I very well understand your feelings and wishes after your numerous incarnations on Earth. You still, however, can decide to stay outside of the Source as an Elohim. And do not forget that Rama will be waiting for Juanzetta, and you after you leave the Earth."

When reading through my diaries again, I found interesting dreams from September 2012 and a record from a meditation which happened shortly after in October 2012. They are related to the process of separating from the Source as a formless Elohim and designing the plan for the spiritual and physical existence. We execute such plan by visiting lower vibrational dimensions and physical planes. After collecting all aspects and experiences and then becoming Chunks of the Infinite Sea of Bonded I-there Clusters, we can return to the Elohim state again. We can then contemplate possibly returning to the Source or continuing a spiritual existence on a different level of understanding for the purpose of our spiritual descent and ascension. Because of that, I was able to understand better and reconnect the descending and ascending aspects of spiritual beings.

I was descending with Juanzetta from a mountain in my dream. We saw a plateau at the bottom, but the descent was not easy. There were huge rocks on the way down and we often had to use ropes to proceed. I was sliding down and offering Juanzetta the support of my body. When Juanzetta told me about her similar dream of seeing us sliding down a hillside helping each other, I knew it was a clear message. Gardener Michael told me in mediation:

"Those dreams symbolize the descent of you as the highest spiritual beings, Elohim, into the lower vibrational dimensions and into the physical plane. Juanzetta and you met early on after your separations from the Source on a remarkably high spiritual level long before you decided to start incarnations into the physical plane, and you got attracted to each other. You decided to help each other as much as possible. Both of you had a strong drive to descend from the high spiritual mountain into the physical C1 environment. That drive also represents your striving for challenges. But I must tell you, Jozef, that it is difficult and rare to meet in C1 as you and Juanzetta did in your current lifetime. And that you fell in love as a man and woman, that is really extraordinary."

Gardener Michael later also told me:

"The decision to incarnate into a physical planetary system is not easy. But once you are there, you can get addicted. Many spiritual beings just start to recycle into reincarnations. And most spiritual beings forget who they were and finding the way back to the Ultimate Source becomes difficult, or completely impossible."

Chapter 16
VISITING A POINT

"Distress not yourself if you cannot at first understand the deeper mysteries of Spaceland. By degrees they will dawn upon you." (Edwin A. Abbott, <u>Flatland: A Romance of Many Dimensions</u>, 1884)

I started to have inquiries about the multidimensional nature of reality early on in my spiritual journey. Curiosity arose when I unexpectedly discovered and read the classical novel *Flatland*, the above quoted ingenious work of Edwin A. Abbott. The book, originally meant as a satire, examined the lowest possible dimensions imaginable in which intelligent beings could live. Abbott described a world with two dimensions where beings live just as if they were like flat creatures living on a sheet of paper.

Abbott also described another world having only one dimension with beings living on a line, and a world with no dimension with beings living in just a point. When I finally thought I fully understood the intentions of Edwin A. Abbott, I asked Michael (as Gardener at that time) several years back, to tell me more about universes with such a small number of dimensions or universes without dimensions as we understand them:

"Do such universes as described in *Flatland* really exist, My Lord?" I asked.

"I want you to clearly understand that Square in Flatland and Monarch in Lineland are as perfectly happy in their two- or one-dimensional space as you are in your three-dimensional space. When they decided to incarnate into those dimensions, they were aware of the limitations being placed upon the temporary residence of their consciousness there under those conditions", said Gardener.

"Can you then tell me more about a Point?"

"A point universe has no dimension; we can call it a zero-dimension universe. You must understand Jozef, that there are countless beings and civilizations living in such universes. The beings living there generally do not need any recognition and understanding of distance or dimension for a happy life. A Point for them contains everything and it is everywhere. Like beings in such a universe can communicate without being aware of any distance, so particles in your own universe can communicate without any distance restriction."

I was wondering if sentient beings really live in a zero-dimension universe and if I could visit them. I decided to try during the first free flow in the Milky Way exercise on the last day of the Starlines Reunion program.

I used my Light Body vehicle with the pilot lights in the base and crown chakras and a slingshot technique to appear in a no space tunnel. After a while, the stars quickly disappeared around me, the tunnel diameter was becoming smaller and smaller, darker, and darker, and I felt denser and denser. I was heading into the Point and soon my perception and feeling of space disappeared.

I heard a loud pop, and I was suddenly in a small bubble. A person sitting in the middle of the bubble in a huge armchair had a crown on his head. He looked like a Burger King from our earthly commercial. I was sitting in a small chair facing him. A table full of lighted electrical buttons was between us. There were small screens all around us on the wall of the round bubble showing a variety of beings doing their seemingly ordinary life activities. I asked him who he was, and he answered:

"I am the King of the Space, and these are my people all around. You should know that dummy! How did you get here and who are you anyway, stranger?"

"I am from the planet called Earth in another Universe, where we have a lot of space for everyone all around us."

"Impossible!" said the King of the Space and continued:

"I am the only one having space by the grace of God! And I give a little space only to those who obey and behave and who deserve it!"

Then the king pushed several buttons on the table and even

smaller screens popped out of the wall of the bubble. It was clear to me that while we could see the people in them, they could not see us.

"When they do not behave, I take space from them. But wait a moment stranger, where is your bubble? I have never heard about your Earth, what is that? I do not need you here, I do not need any rebellion!"

I was withdrawing from the situation while also reminding myself of the Law of Non-Intervention for spiritual travelers. The king was frantically pushing the buttons on his table apparently trying to see me and he was screaming:

"Where are you, where are you?"

I left his space bubble while still being very puzzled about how he was able to create any space at all in a no-dimension point type universe.

Chapter 17
MY FRIEND AND THE GHOST

"Monsters are real, and ghosts are real too. They live inside us, and sometimes, they win." (Stephen King)

In August 2011, I visited my friend in Canada. He is an open minded and spiritually motivated individual. I will call him Fred. During my visit, he again told me the story about the ghost he encountered in the middle of the night when he was 12 years old. He lived in a rural village and needed to go to the outside toilet, because his family did not have one inside. Suddenly, a ghost-like entity came out of the wooden floor in their living room in a gaseous form. Then, it became denser and appeared in front of Fred like a huge threatening monster and raised its arm to hit him. Fred stood his ground and ordered the monster to disappear. The creature was sucked back into the floor and dissolved into the underground. When he was seeking advice about that from his mother, she told him he had been eating too much and was hallucinating. He was always insisting that what happened to him had been very real indeed.

Fred also told me about a very recent incident during which several beings were trying to pull his consciousness out of his body. He felt strong vibrations all over his body and was afraid if they succeeded, he would die. He asked me for some advice. I told him that I would need to go into an altered state for that. It was also for me a welcomed opportunity to see if I could receive information about how to help other people here on the Earth. In a meditation later in my hotel, after setting up my intentions, I called Hadien and asked him if I could see the past and future of other people.

"Of course, you can. That is what many psychics do, and you are also a psychic."

After I described what happened to Fred when he was 12 years old, Hadien continued:

"Your friend obviously encountered a troubled ghost from

the lower astral plane who was looking to infiltrate a human body. They do it often to children and then they can share the body. The child can afterwards have a troubled life and a split personality. Because your friend was a spiritual being who had reincarnated consciously, his Higher Self, or Guardian Angel if you will, was there to alert him and made the effort of the troubled ghost unsuccessful. That is why the ghost was irritated and angry and acted like he wanted to hit Fred, even though he would not be able to do that. The Higher Self or Guardian Angel looked at the ghost through Fred's eyes and the creature had to retreat and disappear."

Then I asked Hadien whether there was a connection between that incident and the recent happenings with several beings trying to pull Fred out of his body. Said Hadien: "Yes, it was the same ghost with some of his low life buddies. If Fred had been forced to raise his vibrations enough to be kicked out of his body at that time, the ghost would have entered his body before Fred could fully return. The ghost could then have stayed in his body and screwed up his earthly life. But Fred's Higher Self or Guardian Angel was there again to prevent it happening."

"What does he need to do if it would happen again?"

"It probably won't, but if it does, he needs to express Love and simply ask such a creature to dissolve and disappear, and it will."

"What is the influence of those situations on his Earthly life?"

"Both times he received spiritual injections from his Higher Self or Guardian Angel. He became more awakened and alert. That is why he is looking for the spiritual purpose of his current life."

"Can something like that happen to me?"

"Not anymore", answered Hadien. "Your protections are on high alert. Troubled and evil beings are looking for those who are more vulnerable. But I do not think that they will ever attack your friend again. They learned their lesson."

Chapter 18
DOLPHIN EXPERIENCE

"When I see a dolphin, I know it's just as smart as I am."
(Don Van Vliet)

Two weeks after the Timeline program in the summer of 2011, I went with Juanzetta to the Wildquest Dolphin Workshop organized on the island of Bimini in the Bahamas. The program was not directly a part of The Monroe Institute, but it was affiliated with TMI and was led by the Monroe outreach facilitators Pamela Boyer and Matthew Joyce. It was supported by the Hemi Sync technology. Before going there, I knew very well that dolphins were not regular mammals. I had read two books about dolphins and gone in meditation to ask Hadien how I should approach dolphins as sentient beings. He told me:

"Approach them as you would approach your brother and your sister."

"Aren't they higher beings, Hadien?"

"Are you not a higher being, Menev? Dolphins do not play that game of who is higher and who is lower. They carry with them respect and kindness for all the living beings they encounter."

"How can I communicate with them? Can I use the ROTE technique?"

"The most important thing is trust. You should show them that you trust them, you respect them, you love them, and you are coming in peace. Then, they might return your trust, your respect, and your Love. They are choosing whom they trust because they do not always have good experiences with you people. They use ROTE all the time. But if you want to have direct communication with them, you must move yourself into an altered state. They are usually in higher vibrations levels than you people, but they lower their vibrations for hunting, feeding, nursing and other necessary daily life activities."

I decided to concentrate on the workshop itself because I knew I did not have enough skills to put myself into an altered state while swimming in the water. Several of the Wildquest crew members were originally from Czechia, which was pleasant surprise for me, and I spoke with them in their language.

A pod of spotted dolphins liked to swim in front of our boat and the crew would play the music of the Swedish group Abba for them. Now whenever I hear "Dancing Queen," I can close my eyes and be back on that boat. Besides several Americans, we also had people from Germany, Sweden, Switzerland, Canada, and Spain in our group. Watching the dolphins hunt fish and pull them out of the sand on the bottom of the sea after they located them with their sonars was utterly fascinating. Swimming above the famous Bimini Road and around the Three Sisters rocks were also highlights of the trip.

However, before we left for home, I had an interesting spiritual experience. It happened on the last day during morning meditation in the Access Channel of Focus 11. After opening the Access Channel, suddenly I felt a dolphin consciousness sliding into my body and pushing part of my own consciousness out. I knew it was none of the three spiritual dolphins I sometimes ask to help me with balancing and healing of my body.

"Who are you and what are you doing my dear friend?" I asked.

"I am Iruka (Iruka is dolphin in Japanese), you are Iruka, we are Iruka, we are One. We want to let you know that because you came here with friendly and loving intentions, we want to reward you with a nice experience. That is why I merged with you, and now we can go for your trip," the dolphin said telepathically.

I felt a strong pull out of my body and suddenly we were at the Three Sisters. I realized that I was a dolphin, and I could do whatever I desired. I wanted to taste fish. We were diving down and pulling fish out of the sand at the bottom of the ocean. I felt the fish going down my throat still moving. I wanted to experience breathing. We sharply rose and I felt strong sea air coming deep into my lungs. I wanted to see the Bimini Road again. We sped over to it and slowed down over the road. I wanted to jump and Iruka quickly took me sharply up from the water. Seconds after, I felt splashing all around me when falling back into the sea.

"If you want to have this experience again, you can find me and call me anywhere anytime," said Iruka and left my body with a chirp. I was crying in my physical body with deep gratitude.

I had a wonderful swimming experience much later, in September 2018, after I had finished the Kindle manuscript of *How to Kiss the Universe*. We were at our favorite Panama City Beach in Florida, and I went to swim in the Gulf. I looked under myself and saw a small manta ray majestically flowing under me. I thought to myself:

"She came to remind me of my wings of freedom."

She made about an eight-foot circle under me and slowly drifted away. I realized that it was a protective circle and was very thankful for that. Then something bumped into my leg. A group of six fishes started to follow me wherever I swam. Even when I decided to go out, they were following me into the shallow water.

Juanzetta commented on the story by saying that it was a thank you from Michael for finishing the book and that he also wanted to show me his continuing support and protection.

Chapter 19
PERPETUUM MOBILE OF LOVE

"All life is a manifestation of the spirit, the manifestation of Love." (Morihei Ueshiba)

One of the last exercises at the Starlines Reunion was about a trans-dimensional link-up. We were supposed to link fragments of our consciousness in the vibrational environment which Robert Monroe would mark as Focus 98 to 105. However, I had already linked all the fragments of my consciousness and created my Chunk of the Infinite Sea of Bonded I-There Clusters. I was well ahead of these exercises, so I decided to do something else. Of course, the frequencies of the exercise took me comfortably on my way. I somehow knew I would meet Michael again, and not just his fragment which resides in me all the time, but a bigger part of his unlimited angelic essence.

However, because I felt that another part of the spiritual journey in my physical body on the Earth was coming to a successful closing, I decided to call on my Council of Star Friends. I met them in the Alpha X Station and thanked them for everything. All of them, except Michael told me that they did not have that much to teach me anymore. However, I knew that they would be there for me anyway if I would need something. My form hugged each one of them and then I asked Michael to stay with me. After he agreed, I asked him if he would show me his Rama.

"Of course, Jozef, but we have to fly out of your Universe." Then our forms headed vibrationally up and I could feel the closeness of Stargate.

"We are in the 12th dimension of your Universe Jozef. That would be Focus 120 in your TMI system and in your imagination. As you know already, God, The Source of Everything is in the 13th dimension."

Then we both grew wings, flapped them, and flew out of the bubble of my Universe. Of course, I did not forget to kiss the membrane. We flew into Michael's Rama and when we were in it, we put our wings down. Michael showed me his beautiful home full of plentiful and colorful gardens, lakes with pristine waters, waterfalls and animal and birds of all kinds lazily moving and flying about in the peace. I recognized only some of them. He showed me also his ball of time and the bender of the space and time. They looked like Juanzetta's and mine which I had seen during my short visit to our Rama. He and I both had young looking human bodies.

"Are you still alone or still looking for someone Michael?" I suddenly asked him that question remembering what he had told me a while ago.

"Not anymore Jozef. Let me introduce to you my significant other. Sweetie, would you come to join us?"

I heard a flapping of wings and looked in the direction of the sound. A woman with coffee-colored skin of incredible beauty with shinning green eyes greeted me with a human hug. She reminded me of the excellent British soccer anchor and analyst Kate Abdo. I asked what her name was:

"My Supreme Love, Clarity, grew up on a forgotten planet deep in the Andromeda Galaxy in similar ways that you did Jozef. I met her in one of my rare embodiments and we fell in love," said Michael.

    I was looking at pretty Clarity with admiration. Then Michael invited me to sit down, and we had glasses of sparkling wine with a delicious taste I had never experienced before. All my manifested body was overcome with joy and ecstasy.

"How is it possible, Michael, that you have all these physical goodies here?" I curiously asked.

"It is not physical, Jozef. All of it is composed of the unconditional Love given to us by the Ultimate Creator. We deserve it for our work, and Juanzetta and you also shall have it after you come home to your Rama."

"I did not decide yet, Michael, what I am going to do. Now that I have the certainty that after my physical death on the

Earth I will reach the Ultimate Choice point, I am not sure if I would be able to face the possibility of incarnation again. I do not want to go to Earth either into a physical body nor as an Ambassador of Love. Jesus tried that and I remember very well what he told me. He shall take care of people on the Earth one way or the other. I am leaving my door for going to Rama open."

I hugged Clarity and Michael with lots of Love, grew my big wings and left, surprised that I could do it alone now without Michael's direct support. Before entering, I kissed our Universe and quickly rejoined my friends meditating at TMI. They were in the Earth Core. I waved my Super-Loosh heart, and it released zillions of its copies into the heart of Mother Gaia. What a wonderful Perpetuum Mobile of Love, I thought to myself, very sure that it was what Mother Gaia needed the most. After that, I heard Darlene Miller's voice reciting Robert Monroe's famous poem:
"There is no beginning, there is no end…"

Sometimes I like to briefly relate the experiences of the other participants which they shared with the group. Janice had an excellent successful experience documenting her power of intention when she realized at the end that she had not played Hemi Sync at all during her meditation. We were all pondering if Hemi Sync could be like a powerful spiritual placebo. Bob was likewise using the slingshot without any support of Hemi Sync. Juanzetta brought her I-There Clusters into the Earth Core to help to collect and remove the bad Loosh from there. Then, she sent the bad Loosh to the special Loosh factory deep in the Universe where it could be converted into good Loosh.

Chapter 20
NEW AFFIRMATION

"Without freedom of thought, there can be no such thing as wisdom." *(Benjamin Franklin)*

After the Starlines Reunion, I was intensively working on finishing and publishing *How to Kiss the Universe*. There was not much going on in my relaxing meditations. Juanzetta suggested us to go to The Monroe Institute for the New Year Program. She had heard only good things about it, so we went for the 2019/2020 program. Problem solving in Focus 12 was one of the first exercises. I had on my TMI shirt with the "I am more than my physical body" motto, and I had my usual three intention questions ready. However, after reaching Focus 12, I received the dictation of my new affirmation instead:

"I am more than my physical body because I can leave it by going beyond its limitations and beyond the Earth Life System.

I can travel through the Galactic Core beyond our Galaxy and the entire Universe.

I can travel into and beyond any other space and time.

I can enter many other dimensions and parallel universes.

I can travel throughout the bubbles of the manifested universes all the way to the Stargate and The Source of Everything.

I can cross through the Stargate into The Source of Everything.

I can enlarge myself beyond any limits.

I can shrink myself beyond any limits and travel inside of living organisms, cells, and manifested matter.

I can reach The Source of Everything in an alternative way by traveling in the microworld.

I will execute my travels only in harmony with unconditional Love. So, help me God!"

Chapter 21
CONSCIOUSNESS AND COMPUTERS

"We recognize that science does not have all the answers. Spirit does." (Lisette Larkins, <u>Listening to ETs</u>, page 87)

My dear friend Peter was one of the top Slovak computer programmers. He is also the one who through his skeptical outlook and approach has kept me from diving too deep into fantasies and eventual hallucinations. I am very thankful to him for that. At the beginning of my spiritual journey, I was always overly excited and eager to share my stories and discuss them with him. He was often comparing some of my interpretations and discoveries with the world of computers. And during our many phone discussions across the ocean, we have found a lot of striking similarities between consciousness and computer networks. I have also often meditated after our conclusions or speculations.

For example, Peter compared my relationship with the universal mind and my guides to the relationship between the server and client in computer networks. The client can use demanded and defined services from the server as I do when I am asking for advice from the universal mind and guides. But the server sees much more into the client than vice versa. Likewise, the much more powerful forces of the universal mind can see much more into the individual mind and brain.

Paul Elder said at an informal discussion in the Lifeline program that the brain is hardware tied to a concrete physical person, whereas consciousness is software and can be downloaded from anywhere into any brain. But the hardware cannot operate or do anything without the software and the software needs an environment or vehicle to be able to execute its intentions. As I discussed with Peter later, the computer's operating system and its internal memory are like that part of consciousness which enables us to exist in the physical environment on the Earth. And, as any user program can be downloaded into any computer memory, anything from the universal mind can be downloaded into any brain. Just like a computer has external memory expanders and has a wide access to the Internet database, we also have external storage for information in a similar database. Some people call such spiritual databases Akasha, the Akashic Library, or other similar names. Spiritual travelers, psychics, mediums, and others use it for a variety of reasons, like for accessing unique information or simply if we do not have enough space in our brain to store all we know. Science has yet to prove its predication that all our memories are stored only in our physical brains.

During the Starlines II program, my spiritual friend Hadien had told me that our computer revolution was triggered by a consciousness flare from the galactic core. According to him, that is why computers and networks are organized like consciousness. He mentioned similarities in memory banks, communication protocols, processors, buffers, interfaces, and peripheral devices.

" I could go on and on" said Hadien and added:

"Just look at your cloud technology. The data which are in the cloud are, in principle, available for everybody. You just must know how to find them, get access to, and download them. Spiritual travelers likewise have to know how to find access and download information from the Akashic Library."

According to the famous theoretical physicist Dr. Stephen Hawking, as he said in an interview with Time Magazine in the fall of 2010, our software mind in the brain stops working when the hardware brain is not there. I would argue: what if that software also had a simultaneous, synchronized copy somewhere else? Then after death it would only need to find another hardware brain in another human body. If that happens, we have reincarnated. But our memories of the past lives are quickly erased for reasons previously discussed in *How to Kiss the Universe* book.

Sometimes in discussions with Peter, we would speculate about the possibility of computer machines rising and enslaving and fighting people as is often portrayed in science fiction books and movies. I asked my guides about this during a trip to the Park while at the Exploration 27 program. Here is what I was told:

"You don't have to worry about your current computers. They cannot revolt because they do not have their consciousness connected to God like living beings have. What you do have to worry about is when you start building computers with a biological base. Malicious consciousness forms can confuse them with living organisms, and they will try to enter them. That is when they will start to mess around with your purpose. If that happens, the Guardians will have to intervene because that whole planet of yours will be in trouble."

A human-made computer can only tap into a digital database created by humans, but not into the Akashic Library. AI cannot tap into an intention of the One, because it is not part of the One. If you know, Dear Reader, how a central processor unit, CPU, works you can understand that concept clearly. Our brain is remarkably like a CPU. A CPU is constantly exchanging information from its internal memory back and forth into its external memory to make its work as effective and fast as possible. Our brain is doing the exact same thing with the Akashic Library.

One of the greatest inventions in information technology happens to be multiprocessing. In my spiritual journey during the New Year program 2019/2020, I saw four spiritual forms from the same earthly time at two different Ramas. My main spiritual teacher and friend Gardener Michael, his lady Clarity, Juanzetta and I were simultaneously in Michael's Rama and our Rama. When I inquired about it, Michael told me:

"You have started to learn spiritual multiprocessing. You can observe, follow, and influence several processes at the same moment of your earthly time. Such skills can enable you to receive a flow of information from multiple sources into a ROTE. You are already very skilled in ROTE unwinding. I must, however, emphasize that such very advanced spiritual skills can be developed and executed only in an environment of unconditional Love. Otherwise, they are reserved for angels or Elohim."

Chapter 22
AI, MACHINES AND US

"Robots today have the intelligence of a cockroach."
(Professor Michio Kaku on NBC, March 2, 2018)

Numerous visionary science fiction writers have for a long time foreseen a future in which we humans would have to fight our own cyber machines or robots. It has also become very fashionable for some spiritual and New Age radio shows in the last several years to speculate about the possibility that we are living in a computer simulated game, in a virtual reality. That way of thinking started to be widely speculated about after the tremendous success of the movie "Matrix" when it was released in 1999. I was intuiting for a long time that the proponents of such ideas did not understand what consciousness really was, even when they were claiming that they were spiritual thinkers.

I decided to ask my spiritual teacher and friend Michael about it in late March 2018. I used the take-home exercise from the Starlines Reunion program which led me into Focus 49 very quickly by riding my Light Body missile. Even though I knew that Michael was inside me, I needed to get far away from earthly vibrational distractions. It worked well, and I asked Michael to explain me his outlook on what we call on our planet Artificial Intelligence:

"First of all, Jozef, I must remind you again that Artificial Intelligence or AI creations do not have silver cords and they are not connected to the One. Therefore, a question about the soul in these creations of yours is irrelevant."

"Well, Michael, our scientists and AI people plan to download the content of the whole human brain into a computer, or into the networks." I said and he answered:

"AI is purely a manifestation of matter and energy. If you would kill a computer, did you kill a human being?

"Obviously not, you just killed an electronic copy of her or his brain. They merely downloaded the content of the human brain into the machine. Moments later, is it the same human being in the machine? It is not, it is just a copy which in a few seconds of its existence in your local space and time is already different than the human brain from which all the information was downloaded. When your Universe would be annihilated and cease to exist, your soul does not need to disappear. It can stay outside of the Source because it has free will. AI does not have free will; it is functioning by use of an algorithm. Free will is a gift from the Source. AI would be destroyed in an annihilation like any other cosmic garbage."

"Thanks, Michael. What do you think? Can scientists create a superhuman?"

"What they call a superhuman would be just a little bit more sophisticated hybrid robot containing biological matter, or a human body containing microchips and other electronic parts and necessary hardware. A superhuman for me, from a spiritual point of view is someone who had gained the permanent spiritual vibrational velocity needed for leaving the Earth Life System. It is someone like you, Jozef, who does not need and does not want to incarnate back on the Earth after the physical death. Spiritual superhumans do not have to reincarnate back to Earth. AI created so-called superhumans, as I said before, are not connected to the Divine Structure of Consciousness. And AI creatures do not have chakras or auras."

I continued in questioning Michael about the difference between Artificial Intelligence and consciousness during the New Year 2019/2020 program. He told me:

"Look, AI needs a sequence to function, consciousness does not. When an AI algorithm stops, AI is stuck and lost, it is not functioning. You can also pull the plug. You cannot pull the plug on consciousness, unless you cross the Stargate for good. When consciousness stops, it is simply in its most natural state of no time and no space, it is in the Sea of Tranquility. When AI stops, it is dead and nowhere until it is started again by an outside intention. AI is a manifested vehicle. Consciousness is not a vehicle; it is a user of a variety of vehicles."

"What about the war of machines against people and against God?", I asked.

'Of course, AI will supersede the intelligence of a cockroach soon and then it can cause a lot of trouble for people in their materially oriented and focused world. Machines could win in a particular space and time, but they can be easily defeated by focused consciousness. Consciousness can create an AI and algorithmic future, but AI cannot create consciousness. The Divine Structure of Consciousness is tied to the Source and the structure of any unit of AI is tied to manifested matter. Matter can be destroyed, consciousness cannot."

Chapter 23
HYBRID TRAVEL

"He who would travel happily must travel light." (Antoine De Saint-Exupéry)

I was often pondering throughout my spiritual journey about whether and how advanced beings could travel extremely long physical distances. I was several times taken in my high vibrational vehicles through black holes into places obviously physically very distant from our planet, thousands or even millions of light years away. I also traveled alone into the highest dimensions of our universe and even outside of our universe in those high vibrational vehicles. I could observe local happenings even in the past or future without the necessity of being physically present in such places. I could create illusions that I was there by appearing in a dense ghost like form for a few moments.

It was quite clear to me that the high spiritual beings like angels and Elohim are using what I would call Spiritual Hybrid Travel Technology involving consciousness stretching by carrying information needed for manifestation and then materialization of the physical body at the destination. I first described what I have learned about such travel in Chapter 88 of *How to Kiss the Universe*.

Obviously, I wanted to know more. Unless our scientists can understand these principles, our travel to other stars and galaxies will stay jokingly local. Never mind that we talk about travelling into the Universe when we are currently only getting a little bit above our planet's atmosphere.

My inquiring about it continued in late March 2018 when I asked Michael to explain to me the difference between a black hole, a wormhole, and the Stargate. He said: "When you are passing through a black hole or wormhole, you are still using your high vibrational vehicle. You travel in a formless energy body that is preventing any harm to you.

You travel usually in the 11th dimension of your Universe. If you are in the 12th dimension, you are in the highest vibrational space in your Universe. You can move out of your universe bubble or travel into another bubble universe only if your dimension and their dimension are vibrationally equivalent and in tune."

"How about the Stargate?"

"When passing through the Stargate, you must drop your energy vehicle; you have to be pure. But you are not godly pure. You become godly pure only after you cross into the Source and permanently stay there. The Source in your Universe is in the 13th dimension, as you know. I hope that you understand that in other bubble universes, it could be and will be in another dimensional number."

I returned to this topic again shortly after arriving to The Monroe Institute for the New Year program. I had learned earlier that such travel uses the Code of Manifestation as described by Michael in my book *How to Kiss the Universe.* He explained to me the difference between the Light Body and the Quantum Body and told me more about manifesting into a physical body when arriving at a destination. He said:

"The Light Body is the highest form of manifested energy and, as such, it can travel up to the speed of light. The Quantum body, by using quantum entanglement principles, can travel by the speed of thought. Consciousness can combine the Light Body and the Quantum Body. The Quantum Body can then carry particles of light by the speed of thought. The particles can be carried to a destination only in limited amounts. These limited amounts are carrying the information which I previously described to you as the Code of Manifestation, remember, Jozef?"

"Are we talking here about spooky action at a distance?"

I was trying to grasp a sense of what Michael was talking about by using the widely known Einstein expression of spooky action at a distance.

"Precisely, Jozef. As your physicists say, particles can exist simultaneously here and there, but they exist only when they are observed. Particles existing here and there can be transferred simultaneously again into a Light Body by the Power of One, the power of consciousness. A Quantum Body traveler can compose her, or his Light Body close to a destination, and then by lowering the vibrations through several dimensions, and by using local dimensional vehicles, can reach the first spiritual body in an astral plane."

"What would such a traveler do then, incarnate into a physical body?" I asked.

"You could do that, Jozef, but you have to be aware of all the consequences of physical life. To carry out your short-term mission, you can appear for an extremely limited time in a denser form which might look like a physical body or a physical form. That is what angels sometime do, but they have to be incredibly careful and be determined not to be lured into a physical incarnation."

Later, I was still curious about other possible ways of hybrid or thought speed travel. I asked Michael at the next opportunity:

"What is the key to reach a speed faster than the speed of light? I travel by the speed of thought in my higher frequency vibrational vehicles, but how does that actually work, my Dear Brother?"

"The opposite of gravity, Jozef, is magnetism, but it is a pure magnetism without electricity. You people on the Earth do not fully understand it, but some of your materialistically oriented scientists and metaphysical travelers such as yourself are getting close to a real advancement. You yourself, Jozef, utilize it very well with the method of sling-shotting your vibrational vehicles through the Singularity Transfer Point."

"Well, I actually have no idea how that thing works, but I know it does my Brother," I answered.

"Almost everyone on your planet is driving or riding in a car and using a smartphone. How many of them understand or know how those things work? Do you really want to know how it works? I could tell you, but I doubt you would understand. You are still limited by constraints of your physical body. You will know these things when you get rid of those limitations."

"Can you tell me at least a bit of it, Michael?"

"To cross beyond the speed of light in your morphed physical bodies, you have to reach an almost pure magnetic power without electricity to eliminate gravity. Magnetic purity multiplies the power of intention and can move a morphed physical object beyond the speed of light. However, your scientists probably cannot solve this issue without cooperation with experienced metaphysical travelers, Jozef."

Chapter 24
SURPRISING HEALER

"In life the only thing that you can expect is the unexpected; the only surprise is a day that has none." (Joan Rivers)

The New Year program was a welcome opportunity for me to do some interesting business in the Earth Life System. Some of the participants had never been to The Monroe Institute before and the exercises never went beyond Focus 27, where the Park is located. On New Year's Day, we had an exercise in Focus 27 with the goal of visiting a Personal Healing Center. An exercise is an individualistic journey, even though participants can sometimes report similar environments and happenings. I need to remark here that there are many more spiritual beings all around us than there are people on the planet. This knowledge should help those of you who are beginners to understand that it is not difficult at all to encounter spiritual beings when you ask. Our Universe is crowded, even though it does not seem to be.

When I got into the Park, I headed directly to my Personal Healing Center. It has a big sign placed above the double door entrance that says "Jozef Menev Skjoerg Plautus Healing Shrine." I stopped flying and walked in in my earthly form. Several nurses dressed in the classical Florence Nightingale nursing style outfits greeted me pleasantly. They were apparently preparing some equipment for my visit.

A youngish looking bald man in a doctor's long white coat walked towards me with a wide joyful smile and gave me a big hug. It was Juanzetta's deceased husband, Dr. Charles E. Flowers. He started to talk:

"I am glad that you finally decided to meet me, Jozef, after all those earthly years of your meditations and the many visits here on the other side. I must tell you, Jozef, I never believed all that talk about this other side Juanzetta was telling me. I must admit though that I am quite happy that my life did not end forever as I thought it would. I have tried to give her signs from here, but that is not easy I am telling you! You can do it only for a few earthly seconds and then you must hurry back. Once, I just ended up in the hardware store not far from where we lived on the Earth. I think one lady who knew Juanzetta and me maybe saw me. But anyway, Jozef, thanks for the interesting presentation of your book you gave on that Viking ship for my society members. How can I help you now, any pains or discomforts in your physical body? I do energy treatments here that can influence physical bodies on Earth. But if you want to do some spiritual adjustments, you have to go to your Light Spa with its Subatomic Accelerator."

"But, Charlie, why are you with me and not with Juanzetta?" I asked.

"I am with her; she is in her Personal Healing Center with me. Are you guys somewhere together on earth right now?"

"Yes, Charlie, we are at the New Year program at a place called The Monroe Institute. We just had a nice welcoming of the New Year 2020 with our group. But how are you with her too, Charlie?"

I was still curious about what was going on.

"Well, I bilocated. It is easy here. After I realized that I could continue without my physical body, I tried it right away and it worked! I am already healing Juanzetta in her Personal Healing Center, so what do you need now, Jozef?"

"I have recently developed mild pain in my shoulders. Can you do something about it?"

"Put him in the balancer!" Charlie nodded toward his nurses.

The nurses positioned me in a booth which reminded me of the scanners at our airports, and they closed the unit. Charlie started to operate the device. Two big coils from the sides of the unit started to move and cycle around my shoulders and the upper part of the body by moving up and down along my chakras. That lasted several earthly minutes. When I stepped out of the healing unit, Charlie told me:

"I did energy balancing in those areas, but it can take a few earthly days to bring your shoulders and the top part of your body into full balance."

Then I asked him to let me see Juanzetta in her healing center. He switched on a giant screen, and I saw him doing a similar procedure with Juanzetta.

"She looks incredibly young for her age. What are you doing with her, man, that she looks so good?" He seemed to be surprised.

"Well, I love her so much, Charlie, because she is a giver. I am not that good, and I am also fully occupied with trying to promote my book. You know, partner, we had an exercise in the New Year program to write down the three most influential and important people in our lives. You, Charlie, you made it into her top three; I did not, she put me in as number four in the exercise. She was my number one. But I am her spiritual soulmate, while you are one of her guides now. We will sort it out after Juanzetta and I leave the Earth. We are all One anyway!"

We hugged and I flew back to Nancy Penn Center to rejoin my group and the program.

Chapter 25
FIVE MESSAGES AGAIN

"When you want something, all the universe conspires in helping you to achieve it." (Paulo Coelho)

The Five Messages exercise from the Gateway Voyage program at The Monroe Institute builds up the ability to receive utterly important messages in a simple easy to understand form. I described my fabulous Five Messages in *How to Kiss the Universe*. Likewise, your trained mind can formulate strategic intensions also in a simple easy way to help you remember them for use in the future.

In July 2017, Juanzetta and I took part in a Progressive Workshop led by the well-known motivational and meditation teacher, Dr. Joe Dispenza, in Atlanta, Georgia. One of his exercises was about blessing your body, life, and soul. My mind, already well-trained from the Gateway Voyage and many other programs at TMI, formulated my specific blessings into another five messages. Here is the talk to my body:

5. I love you and I will take care of you.
4. I will listen to you.
3. However, I will not serve you; you shall listen to me and serve me until our last moment.
2. I am a divine, unlimited, and timeless being. I just occupy you temporarily until I go back home.
1. I bless and love my body, bless, and love my life, and I bless and love my soul.

Some other surprising results I received during the New Year program 2019/2020 happened when we practiced the Gateway Voyage exercise of Five Messages in Focus 12. I asked the Universe, my guides, Star Friends and even the Source itself to give me guidance about how to execute the Ultimate Decision. I was still struggling a little bit with it. While driven by my Love throughout the ages to Juanzetta as described in *How to Kiss the Universe*, I was also considering a complete and irreversible return to The Source of Everything. Juanzetta and I were at that time also pondering about eliminating one of our two residences and living in only one place together. And there were no doubts that we would choose to live only in Birmingham, Alabama and not in Washington, D.C.

The exercise is voiced by Robert Monroe himself, and that alone is enough for me to receive rich and meaningful results.   To make sure of having truthful messages, I put any Front Loading into my Security Repository Box. That way, it could not disrupt me with any wishful thinking while meditating. Here are the new five messages I received:

5. Eliminate all your doubts about living with your Juanzetta in one place for the remaining years of your physical life on the Earth.

4. You can make your Ultimate Decision in front of the Stargate only after the final exit from your physical body.

3. Before you make your Ultimate Decision, you must give Juanzetta the chance to make her decision first.

2. Juanzetta and you should confer with your spiritual guides about your Ultimate Decisions before you make them. You can do it separately or together.

1. Before you approach contemplation about your Ultimate Decision, you must first analyze and evaluate all your spiritual activities and accomplishments.

I am also including here Juanzetta's Five Messages from the same program. While mine were intended to help me with my spiritual decision, Juanzetta's messages were simply beautiful. Here they are:

5. There is no ending and no beginning. There is only Is! You are! Wherever you are in the Universe, you are!

4. You are a beloved child of the Universe. You were sent here in Love, and you have done what you came to do. You have completed your Task.

3. You are powerful ancient woman wisdom. You are a Goddess and contain goddess energy in your Being.

2.   All life is One. All life is sacred; honor it with your thoughts and actions.

1. You will return to Rama from which you came. That is your reward for a life well lived and a Task well achieved.

Chapter 26
PARABLE OF A BOWL

"Don't judge each day by the harvest you reap but by the seeds that you plant." (Robert Louis Stevenson)

I have documented the importance and power of dreams for any spiritual traveler in both of my books. During my spiritual travels, however, I was often wondering how much our dreams reflect our lives in the physical environment we call C1 in the Monroe model of exploration. Those who do not believe in anything, but physical reality would tell you that dreams are only a reflection of our physical reality. Some years back I asked Gardener about this, and I want to share his parable with you. He said:

"Imagine a big bowl of wheat grains or rice or any other small seeds under a cover in a bowl. The seeds are your thoughts, memories, connections, everything you have learned. The cover of the bowl is a membrane to the outside world, to everything that exists outside of you. You can vigorously shake the bowl with the cover on, you can turn it sideways or upside down, and what you are going to get? All the same grains are still there; you have only changed their configuration. That is what the people who do not believe in the power and importance of dreams are doing; they are keeping the grains isolated in the bowl," said Gardener and continued:

"When you open your mind and take the cover off, you can take out your grains, trade them or give them away and even get new ones. You can remix them in your bowl again and again, because you have crossed the membrane into an infinite and unlimited reality. And as you know, Menev, we like your grains, and we create for you a lot of interesting, uplifting, and educational dreams from those grains."

Chapter 27
POWER OF MIND

"The mind is everything. What you think you become." (Buddha)

I had an immensely powerful dream on May 28, 2011. I was somewhere with a group of guys who were picking on me and making me feel miserable. I said to myself: "I am now going to show you who I am!"

I started to fly and formed into a horizontal tornado with a big mouth like would normally be at the bottom of the tornado. My mouth was blowing a tremendously powerful stream of air, and just by turning it in the direction of my tormentors, I scared them to death.

I quickly lost interest in them and flew toward my childhood house in the village of Láb where I was born. I realized I was a Hindu God and perceived the name Vishwanath. I was making strong scary sounds: "Vuuu...vuuu...vuuu!" When I approached the house, I shrank into such a small size that no one could detect me, and I woke up. That was the first time that I realized I could shrink my consciousness.

The next day I went into meditation. When I opened my Heartgate, I started to feel Love coming into my heart in a homogenous stream. My heart was sucking it up like a whale shark is sucking up plankton. At the same time, I felt Loosh streaming out of my heart, but it was shaped into a variety of forms. I asked for the Gardener. He came and I said:

"Thank you, Your Majesty. I am very humbled and thankful that you are paying attention to me. I would like to understand my dream."

"I am glad that you came. You needed to dream about your powers. Now shape yourself as it happened in the dream!"

I started as a small tornado-like shape which was growing into galaxy size and then shrinking back. But all the time, my mouth was blowing out a stream of tremendously powerful energy. Said Gardener:

"Up to now you understood your unlimited nature as the ability to get as big as you wanted and as small as you wanted, the ability to get anywhere in no time and spin as fast or as slow as you wanted. But now, we have given you Blowing Power which represents your unlimited ability for action. You can use your accumulated energy whether you want to scare your enemies or do something good. Yes, you are as powerful as Vishwanath-Shiva. Try to blow away the stars and you will see!" I did and the stars receded.

"Can I really do that?" I wondered. Gardener smiled and said:

"You can do that with your mind and in your mind. You obviously cannot move the physical stars; I cannot do that either. But if it is happening in the mind, you can do anything just as you did when you shrank the Universe and held it in your hand."

"Why did I go as Vishwanath-Shiva to the house where I was born?

"You went to the roots of your current earthly existence. You became small and hidden because you did not want to abuse your powers, but you wanted to be ready if they would be needed. You received the spiritual powers you have now through modifying your DNA when you were born. You just had to discover them and that has just happened."

A couple of years later, in January 2013, one of my spiritual friends whom I call Ra was reminding me about the warrior spirit when doing metaphysical exploration. According to him, the fighting spirit of an explorer can significantly contribute to the raising of one's power of mind. Yet, he also was emphasizing that any fight needs to be fair, and he explained Spiritual Integrity to me:

"If you are in the physical C1, you can control all you do and often successfully reach a desired goal or result. When you are in meditation, you can only try to control and direct your intention. You cannot control a goal or result. But you can learn how to control your dreams when you master the art of lucid dreaming. You shall progress more if you unify your efforts in all three, physical C1, meditation and dreams. The goal and your actions in those three states, when you are fully aware in the physical, when you are in an altered state, and when you are dreaming should be the same, only the tools and methods are different. And when you reach that, you will have accomplished Spiritual Integrity. You should strive for that whether you go into the metaphysical world consciously or subconsciously. Who you are should be reflected the same way in all three states of your consciousness."

Chapter 28
TRUST

"The best way to find out if you can trust somebody is to trust them." (Ernest Hemingway)

The question of mutual trust was a significant issue contributing to my early doubts in my communications with the guides and star friends who appeared from time to time. When I was sharing my experiences with my skeptic friend, he was often giving me advice of what to ask them and how. And, at times, he was also suspicious that they were trying to deceive and manipulate me. He was always insisting that they were most likely manipulating and using people all the time, and that we could not do anything about it.

I was confident that our own minds looked out for us. Nonetheless, the influence of my friend on me has always been strong, and I continue to admire him. Here is what happened on August 31, 2009, when I entered an altered state:

"It seems to us that you have issues with us. It looks like you are thinking about not trusting us!"

I realized that they had just read my mind. They continued:

"None of us can tell you lies from here if you don't allow it. We are you and you are us! Do not bring limitations here because they will impede your progress! You do not want to destroy your accomplishments. Remember what your friend Gene Taylor told you and do not bring suspicions and limitations here!"

And, suddenly, Gene was standing there smiling at me just like in his picture on the wall at The Voice of America. The meditation was at night and Gene was probably sleeping, but my guides asked his spirit to show up in support. He did not say anything, he just smiled. And my guides repeated several times:

"Here the most powerful are those who have the strongest thoughts!"

In another exercise, my guides reminded me about the existence of a barrier between the physical and spiritual worlds which had been created by the Guardians. The Guardians had decided to build the barrier after the easy entrance into the spiritual realm was abused by the Atlanteans. The Guardians decided that the experiences and emotions from the physical would be stronger when the existence of the spiritual world could not be proven on our planet.

Today, it appears that people on Earth are devoting their time overwhelmingly to the material world. The guides told me:

"Only those who put effort into it like you do can find the narrow channels we left for access to the reality of the so-called Other Side."

According to the Guardians, people on Earth generally use just one percent of their Higher Selves. They can increase the level of usage by downloading up to fifteen percent from the spiritual realm such as the people known as geniuses or prodigies, or avatars are able to do. After I asked about myself, they told me that I was at three percent at that time.

There is also another especially important aspect of this effort. Clusters of spiritual entities in the upper levels of the Earth Life System are connected through these channels to awakened people on Earth, and to spiritual and sacred places on Earth. This creates a protective grid that is spiritually guarding our whole planet. Here is what they told me during my MC Squared program:

"Well, Menev, you are one of those persons who, besides being able to pass through the crust of the Earth Life System, are also trying to break it or make big holes in it. We encourage passing through the barrier, but you must understand that the creators manifested the Earth Life System and its boundaries for a reason. You can continue your mission by going through the crust as often as you want; just do not try to create a big hole in it, because you will not succeed, and you will just waste your energy. The crust will be removed only when everybody inside the ELS has spiritually grown enough to understand the true essence of their being and where their true home is in unity with the Ultimate Creator. When that happens, everyone can go to this true home."

The crust is the upper spiritual ring around our Earth Life System, and it is between the vibrational levels of Focus 27 and Focus 35. This might be the reason that most of the activities of psychics and other spiritual mediums and explorers are conducted inside the Earth Life System.

However, this does not prevent anybody from venturing wherever they desire to go if they have enough courage and determination to do so. And many revolutionary spiritual explorers do.

Chapter 29
DIVINE WE

"Only complete spiritual beings can accomplish a return to the Source." (How to Kiss the Universe, Chapter 88, by Author)

One of the exercises at the New Year Program was the Tree Exercise in Focus 18. Focus 18 in the Robert Monroe model is a place of Love, heart, and emotions. I naturally set up the intention to talk about how we are loving God, our life partners, children, family, and strangers. I got into Focus 18 very quickly and started my questioning without thinking about whom I was questioning:

"Can we talk about a loving God and her or his Love?"

"We shall be talking not only about God's Love, but also about your Love. You became so powerful because you are not faking it. You are telling the truth and spreading the truth. There is a lot of faking around you, however. Because you discovered and are practicing trips to get close to God, you are strong. The closer you come to God, the stronger you become until you are ready for your Ultimate Graduation. You and Juanzetta are aiming to live in the place where only unconditional Love abides."

Then I heard Darlene Miller's voice in the headphones to pick up the key and open the heart.

"Thank you, Dar, please forgive me, but this time I shall be fully sailing alone. My heart is already opened and my Heartgate is spurting rose and green geysers," I said in my mind and continued in my questioning:

"Are only angels living in those places of unconditional Love?"

"Yes, indeed and they have no direct connections to the manifested universes. Unconditional Love exists only in those places which are completely outside of manifested universes, as you know."

"What about the unconditional Love we talk about on our

planet, for example, we say that dogs love us unconditionally?"

"That is just to make you feel good. While it is certainly beautiful on your physical planet, you must understand that your dog loves you simply because you are giving her or him food and shelter. Love between lovers or parents and children can be also beautiful in the physical world, but it is always beneficial for participants, and sooner or later can become compromised."

"How then would we go for our various incarnations into the many universes?" I asked surprised.

"That is the lure to see if you are really ready. You can do that, but then you obtain your silver cord structure again all way to the manifested matter. If you are not careful enough, you can become a Fallen Angel. If you want to stay in Rama forever, you must operate in manifested universes only as an angel, or archangel or however you call such uncompromised spiritual godly beings on your planet. We are extremely strict about our angels."

I realized I had talked to the *Source*, God herself, himself, or themselves. The Source used We in our conversation for the first time ever. I decided to call The Source of Everything as the Divine We. Then I continued in my conversation:

"What about my teacher and friend Michael and his lady Clarity? Do they incarnate?"

"No, they don't. When you asked him about his incarnations, he was talking about his past in your earthly understanding of time. He is incredibly careful not to become a Fallen Angel. He saw many of his friends being lured into incarnations and the goodies of physical life and they fell from angel status. He was just teasing you!"

And I had a lot to think about again. I however continued in conversation with the Divine We when they were willing to talk to me:

"What about loving children?"

"You lead them to learn the same way you did. You tell them

the truth, lead them to practice the truth and practice the real Love. If they do not want to accept and follow you, let them find their true ways in their future lives. They are related to you through your genes, but they are completely different spiritual individuals. That applies even if they are in your spiritual group, and/or they chose you by incarnating into your family."

"How can we love and teach strangers?"

"You can teach them similarly as you do your children, with the advantage that they are not tied to you through genes. You can freely choose those who are spiritually more advanced and open to learn more."

And the conversation was over.

Chapter 30
DANIEL

"Daniel, you're a star in the face of the sky. Oh, Daniel my brother... (From the song by Elton John and Bernie Taupin)

It was the night before my Name Day, which I still celebrate. Jozef's Day in Czechoslovakia, celebrated on March 19, used to be the top drinking day of the year. Not only is the name Jozef probably the most common male name, and the name of Christ's biological father, but it is also called the day of men's revenge. In the old by communists governed country, March 8 was celebrated as the International Day of Women. On this day, some ladies would come home after drinking a little bit. That provided a reason for many men to heavily drink eleven days later:
"What, you could drink a few days before and now I cannot?!"

I was sentimentally remembering some of my memorable Jozef's Days escapades while obviously sober because no one celebrates a name day in the USA. I guess a name is nothing to be celebrated. One of the first American members of my family remarked when learning about the custom:
"That is really stupid!"

I was lying in my bed alone in Washington D.C. at 11 pm and getting ready to go back to my beloved Birmingham in Alabama to join Juanzetta there. I had suggested for her to stay in Birmingham because the coronavirus pandemic had just started to burgeon and threaten everybody. I had a 750-mile drive ahead and just wanted to sleep. I decided to play the Starlines Reunion CD and put on my headphones. I put Covid19 into the Energy Conversion Box at the beginning of the exercise. I also created a Protective Energy Balloon specifically for not allowing the virus to enter my body. And then I went to sleep.

Those who meditate with Hemi Sync know how often

it can put you sleep when you would like to have a good meditation, especially when you have paid good money for the program. Most people call it clicking out. But it also works very well in the opposite way, as you will learn from what follows.

  While believing I was sleeping, I appeared at Alpha X Station in Focus 49. Michael greeted me there waiting with his wings widely spread and mine grew as big as his immediately.

"I have something for you, My Brother," Michael said and started to play the song *Daniel* sung by Elton John.

"Why do you play that song, Michael, what's up?"

"I can be a little sentimental too, Jozef. It is a good feeling. You told me goodbye at the end of your book *How to Kiss the Universe*. I saw your taillights leaving too, even though you thought that you saw only mine when we parted.

  I was not able to imagine what was ahead for Daniel and me and all those wonderful happenings are described in the latter chapters. Without any planned intensions, I immediately asked Michael if we could go to his Rama.

"Of course, My Brother!" said he and the bubbles of the universes were all around us and passing us as we landed in the cylinder. He put down his wings and asked me to do the same. I did and we sat beside a small table in unbelievably comfortable armchairs. A bottle appeared with two crystal clear glasses.

"What is that My Lord?"

I was in awe, not even imagining that it was possible we were going to have a drink.

"Congratulations on your Name Day, My Brother! I got the Chartreuse Liquor for you to taste. You always wanted it and here it is for you even before you planned to open your physical bottle. It just came yesterday by UPS, didn't it?"

We tasted it and it was heavenly delicious.

"How can it taste so great like it would on a physical plane?"

"Rama is waiting for you, Jozef, and for Juanzetta. Everything here because it is composed from unconditional

Love is at least as good as in the physical. Of course, many things are so good that I am not even able to describe them to you. It is the best stuff out of the many manifested universes and planets such as yours, and even those that are more diversified, rich, and beautiful. Look at those two young human bodies without any flaws and illnesses, they are waiting for you. All of that is the Ultimate Creator's gift for both of you for your growth and work and for returning a lot of multiplied unconditional Love to the Source."

I looked around and again saw the incredibly rich beauty of colorful flowers, birds, plants, and animals. The landscape reminded me the Napali Coast of Kauai, but it was even more breathtaking.

"Is this a True Heaven, Michael?"

"You can say so, but look, Jozef! You have nothing to do on the Earth anymore, you are not only a Graduate, but an Ultimate Graduate. Do not be disappointed about *How to Kiss the Universe* was received. It has happened to us on other planets and moons all over your Universe and in the other universes. When obsession with material life and greed reaches uncontrollable proportions, that kind of thing happens. People do not want to listen to you, they are not interested. Many will be staring into their phones for the rest of their physical lives without even noticing the beauty around them. You and Juanzetta have finished what you came to do on your planet. It is time for you to go home! It can be tomorrow, or it can be in many years before you depart. Just enjoy your freedom and all you have built and all you have. However, I cannot help you with the deposition of your physical bodies. Just enjoy your last days on your planet before you ease out."

I thanked my dear teacher and brother and left to go back to the Earth. In the morning, I felt tremendously energized and played *Daniel* by Elton John from my smartphone through my car stereo at least twenty times, if not more, while driving back to Alabama. Ten days later, March 29, when I was back in Birmingham, it was the day when my younger son Boris has his birthday. The celebration of my Name Day with Michael at Rama was fresh in my memory, and I decided to meditate to see what would happen. I was using the Starlines Reunion CD again and was heading to the Alpha X Station in Focus 49.

When I arrived, Michael was already there waiting for me, and I went straight to the point:

"What about that business with Daniel, Michael?"

I obviously impolitely started our conversation, but then continued:

"What does it mean?"

"You always loved that song, didn't you, My Brother? But you never asked me about why, did you? You were Daniel a long time before you were Plautus in your local space and time."

Then, he showed me the scene of four young men humbly standing and kneeling in the front of Nebuchadnezzar's throne.

"Do you see yourself as Daniel, Jozef?"

And I saw myself.

"That is why you can work with your dreams so effectively," said Michael and added:

"You were travelling around a lot making sure that people who would harm you were not following you. You were quite afraid, and you used several different identities."

Chapter 31
SHRINKING

"Entering a cell, penetrating deep as a flying saucer to find a new galaxy would be an honorable task for a new scientist interested more in the inner state of the soul than in outer space." (Dejan Stojanovic)

Throughout my spiritual journey, I was often having the desire to be able to enter as consciousness into the microworld, especially into our human cells. Scientists and many people in the public are aware of the complexity of cells, especially those in the brain. Our cells can be compared to the complexity of the Universe. I described some of the implications of that in Chapter 44 of my book *How to Kiss the Universe.*

I asked Michael about the possibility of entering the microworld at the New Year Program during the Problem-Solving Exercise in Focus 12. He told me:
"You would have to travel in a modified and shrunken form toward your destination. You could then enter the cell like a virus or bacteria would. If you would like to manifest there, you must be completely sure that you are at the desired physical location. If you were able to manifest inside the cell, then you could modify it or even kill it. But that is not easy, it is a very advanced technique."

I was again pleasantly surprised that I was able to receive a good result despite using the lower vibrational level of Focus 21. It seems the lower levels can also work very well for solving any Earth Life System issues and inquiries. I continued to ask about shrinking and entering the physical body as consciousness at the cell level. I learned from him:
"You first have to move your consciousness into a higher dimension. The best would be the middle transitional dimension. According to your earth numbering, it would be the eighth dimension. You would go there to modify your spiritual vehicle into the shape of a ball. The higher you go,

the easier it is to do it. Then you start the process of shrinking in that dimension by condensing your ball vehicle into the size of a virus. To get to the cells, you bring your virus sized ball vehicle through the outer layer of your physical body. That way you enter cells as a spiritual being using that vehicle like a virus would. When you are at your destination, you can materialize. If you need to multiply, you first multiply your vehicle into as many balls as the number of cells you want to enter. That way you can execute multiple entries and multiple manifestations to modify cells or even kill them."

"Can I change the DNA that way?" I asked.

"Yes, you can, but you need more time to learn that."

I was eager to try it immediately. I focused on my painful arthritic finger on the right hand. I entered it as I had been directed and expressed the intention to find the inflamed cells and tame the pain. The pain stopped in few seconds. I then returned to the eighth dimension as a ball. Then, I transformed into my regular spiritual form in that dimension before returning to my physical body through the lower dimensions using a variety of different descending vibrational energy vehicles.

Chapter 32
MICRO-TALKS

The Disclaimer and the Warning: This chapter is about the Covid19 virus. It does not challenge or dispute the instructions of the legal and medical authorities or say how you should proceed in case you become infected, or by any other way interacting with Covid19. If you feel that you already have strong opinions about Covid19 and my writing could affect that in a harmful or undesirable way, please do not read this chapter. Just proceed to the next one. If you do read this chapter, know I am not responsible for any eventual medical or material damages resulting from your actions.

"Nothing in life is to be feared, it is only to be understood. Now is the time to understand more, so we may fear less."
(Marie Curie-Sklodowska)

I started writing this chapter in the first half of 2020, when the worst Covid 19 situation in the United States was in New York City. After the marvelous and shocking revelation by Michael about Daniel and me, I decided to ask him about the coronavirus. It was late March, and I was happy to have returned to Alabama to be with Juanzetta. The virus had just started to terrify the whole planet. Michael obviously read the worries in my mind and said:

"Look Jozef, it really does not matter if you leave the Earth now or later. Rama is waiting for you and Juanzetta to arrive. You did what you came to do on your planet. And it also does not matter if you write your second book or not. Think of that effort as your hobby which is making your last days, weeks, months or years pleasurable, creative and productive in that order."

"But Michael, how can I help people fight the coronavirus?"

"Shrink your higher dimension vehicle and challenge the virus's consciousness. As you probably suspect already, a virus is an integrated consciousness body. Therefore, you can shrink yourself into the virus's structure size and talk to him or her. You can even try to enter the virus's consciousness body or his or her individual biological units and move them away from people. But those actions are not easy to execute." I received the call to go back to Earth and had a lot to think about.

I went into action the next day angry and combative. I put all my consciousness size limitations into the Energy Conversion Box. I also created a Protective Energy Balloon around my own consciousness vehicle with the receptors outside, like the virus has. However, I received a warning not to have them and so I removed them and travelled without them. When I detected the eighth dimension's vibrations, I stopped my vibrational movement upward and started to transform my form into a ball shape. Then, I shrank my vehicle into a coronavirus size and directed it into an infected patient's body in New York City.

"What the hell is that?" I heard a voice.

"It is a defective comrade!" I heard another voice.

"Just kill him, it's an enemy!" I heard a third voice.

The coronaviruses about my size started to jump on me, but they could not do anything. I did not have any receptors outside of my consciousness vehicle ball. They could not engage with me at all.

"Do not even try, you cannot kill me. You could kill my physical body, but not me. Tell me, are you one or many?" I challenged them.

"We are the one with many arms, with thousands of millions of arms. We are like an octopus with thousands of millions of arms!" I heard the answer.

"Are you alive or not? Can you sleep?" I asked.

"What do you think, smart ass?"

"You are alive, because you carry bad intentions and information, and you can reproduce and eat!" said I.

"And we are gonna eat you, we are gonna eat you all. You are just food. You eat everybody else in nature thinking they are just food, and now, we are going to eat you all! You are not one anymore, you are changed to many! We are one and we are going to eat the whole lot of you! We were here long before you and we shall continue to be here long after we kill you all," answered the self-described virus octopus.

Now I really got angry:

"I am ordering you now to disappear, to leave the bodies of all humans on the Earth and go back to your pangolin or bat, or wherever you came from! Or go to sleep somewhere! You can sleep because you are alive. Leave immediately! I am ordering you to do that in the name of the greatest teacher ever, in the name of the Lord Jesus Christ! I am Daniel who foretold his coming here and now I am here as his humble servant!"

I was screaming and then I heard a squeaky, scary defeatist sound. The thousands of millions of arms Octopus was rapidly shrinking and disappearing into the distance. But I knew the nasty creature had just retreated from the human body we were in so it could be out of my sight, and that it might return to that body.

My virus size vehicle inflated into a larger size ball during my return to the eighth dimension. I increased the size of the ball back into my spiritual form and came back to the physical feeling like I had had a good fight.

I tried again about a week later. I used the same technique but created a thick crust on my vehicle ball and kept the receptors turned inward from the crust. I directed myself back into the woman's body lying in the Elmhurst hospital. I also created protection balloons for all the cells in my body and protection balloons for Juanzetta, my family and friends. When I reached the destination, I heard:

"You are here again, stranger, your effort is worthless. Go back home, we are going to kill you all!"

I started to feel a scratching in my physical throat, so I ordered all the cells in my physical body not to engage with the virus. Then I started to express my feelings:

"You are not going to kill us all, buddy! You are just a primitive vicious killer. You are greedy! Unlike you, we create, you do not! All you can do is viciously mutate and kill some more. Kill, kill, kill! If you were smart, you would keep us alive so you could be a parasite on us. But you do not, you are a stupid Son of a Bitch! Get out of our bodies!" I was angry. But the Octopus started to reason:

"Mother Earth asked me to attack you. You are like a cancer on her skin. She has had enough of you; she wants to get rid of you."

"You are a liar, Octopus. I do not believe you. Our Mother Gaia might be angry at us because we did and do make a lot of mistakes. But we can also love and be compassionate, and we help each other. She knows that if we change our ways, we can make her beautiful again, we can heal and cherish her skin. We can and will change and live with her in harmony again. You better disappear and leave us alone, Octopus!"

My ball started to inflate and soon I joined the flow of the exercise to get back to the physical through the transformational eighth dimension.

After I described my experiences to Juanzetta, she suggested I use a friendlier, curious, and more polite tone in my conversation with the virus. She also suggested I try another locality, like the University of Alabama in Birmingham, and ask the virus Octopus if they wanted something from us, and why they are doing what they are doing. I used the same technique through the eighth dimension and entered a human body at UAB. I was not surprised when the virus Octopus recognized me immediately. The virus is an integrated body of consciousness indeed.

"Again you, what do you want?" I heard.

"Please, I am coming now in peace. I want to know you, I want to learn about you," I said.

"Well, you were cocky, and I was cocky. No one of your kind has talked to me yet, except for you anyway," answered the virus.

"I love you my friend, even though you are killing us. I apologize for being arrogant. I would like to understand, what you would really like to do with us."

"Really? Well, this is the only life we can have. All we can do here is just eat protein, no other fun," said the virus Octopus and continued:

"I hate this planet. Life for us here is difficult and boring. It is awfully hard for us to go from body to body. We must lose a lot of limbs again and again. It is painful for us, you know, my human friend."

"Why are you calling yourself "we"? You told me you are one. How come?" I asked.

"I have here sisters, brothers and cousins, other variations of us that you call viruses. They must do the same as I do, and I speak for all of them. We are We, but also, I am I! I am the Protein Queen!"

"Is that your name?"

"Yes, our being here is very annoying. We want to go back home!" the virus Octopus was whining.

"Where is your home my friend?" I asked.

"Far away. It was a beautiful place, our planet. We lived in a large protein ocean. We were enriching and entertaining the ocean and the ocean was giving us food. We lived together in great harmony. We were creating beautiful structures for her all the time. The ocean loved it and we were happy."

"What happened, why did you come here?" I was curious.

"Our planet was hit with something big from space and then she exploded. We travelled millions and billions of years on a small rock until it hit this place. It is beautiful for you, but not for us. We always lose when we try to grow bigger, and we have to shrink again and again."

"How is it that you know our languages?" I wanted to know.

"We are bothering you from time to time because we want and need to survive. We have also been watching you and listening to you for ages and we have learned a lot. Finally, at least one of you is now talking to us. Please, help us!"

I listened to the creature and told her:

"I love you my friend, but I do not know how to help you. However, you could be nicer to us. Why do not you modify again? You can live in your flexible structure forever, unlike we people. Maybe you just could sleep and wait for a big meteor, asteroid, or comet to hit our planet in the future and then you can again catch a ride to look for a better place to live. Sooner or later, you can be kicked out into space and find another protein planet."

"Do you really think that could happen?"

"Yes, my Protein Queen, in a short time for you, but probably a long time for us. I hope that our planet will have an apocalypse only when it is dying from old age and all the people have all gone to another suitable place. However, you can also get lucky and be carried away by our spaceships in the future. For now, please mutate into a different form that will not kill us please, Miss Protein Queen Virus Octopus with thousands of millions of arms. Don't forget that I love you and wish you well."

And the signal in the headphones called me back to my physical body.

Chapter 33
INTO A CHIP

"Neutrinos, this invisible sea of particles is the lifeblood of the universe." (From Through the Wormhole with Morgan Freeman)

On one September 2020 Sunday exactly at 1 pm, I approached my TV and subconsciously pushed the power button on the remote. I looked at the screen and saw the title of movie which had just started. It was "Matrix." A long time ago, when I had just started to go out with Alenka, I invited her to see our first movie together. It was "Matrix", the wrong choice. After several scenes, I looked at her and she was having a nap. I was worrying about her and many scenes for me just went by unnoticed or not fully understood. Later I learned that when Alenka did not like a movie, she would always fall asleep. It was completely normal for her.

On that September Sunday I remembered that I had missed a lot from the movie the first time and so I stayed stuck to the screen this time. Then, I learned that the name of Morpheus's ship was the Nebuchadnezzar. As I described earlier, my dearest teacher Michael had shown me a scene in which I was Daniel standing in front of King Nebuchadnezzar's throne with three of my friends. It was clear to me that synchronicities do not happen just randomly. I knew I had to go into meditation and did so the next day with the Starlines Reunion CD.

I was not surprised, when I reached Focus 49, that Michael was there already waiting for me. And I asked him: "Dear Brother, obviously you wanted me to see the "Matrix" movie again. Can you tell me why?"

"Jozef, you are interested in Artificial Intelligence as she tries to enslave the people who created her. You understand that consciousness is the way to defeat her if such a threat would become apparent. I would like to send a message to the people of your planet that there is a better way to fight and defeat AI machines than how it was portrayed in the "Matrix".

"Can I use the technique of shrinking you taught me earlier, Michael, and infiltrate AI hardware structures? I had great experiences communicating with the Corona virus. So, I would like to know how I could enter the hardware microworld like computers or even chips. It seems to me that the keys to disrupting malevolent microelectronic structures are in the consciousness presence right there."

"That is correct, Jozef but your vehicle needs to be much smaller than the one you used to enter human biological cells. You have to go beyond the atomic level."

Meanwhile, the meditation guidance was taking us to the proximity of the Milky Way's black hole.

"Look into the black hole, Jozef. I have manifested an interesting stream for you. Do you see them?"

I looked and saw a steady stream of what looked like rays, but it was obvious that it was a stream of particles.

"What are those, my Brother?" I asked.

"Do you remember, Jozef, years back when Juanzetta was reading a little book to you while you were driving on a trip? I gave her the signal to select that book. It was about amazing particles. Do you remember, Brother?"

"Neutrinos! Wow! Is that what this stream of particles is composed off, Michael?"

"Exactly Jozef, and I hope you realize that we are in the eleventh vibrational dimension."

"What should I do?"

"Unlike you were shrinking your consciousness for entering the cell in the eighth dimension, for a trip into the subatomic level, you have to come here. You start your shrinking here and use the neutrino as your vehicle. It is a vehicle and when you merge with it, you can speed it up or slow it down like any other vehicle. Do not be intimidated by its speed, which can be faster than the speed of light. You travel by speed of thought, don't you? Just grab a neutrino and go! You can then direct it into the computer, chip, or microchip of your choice. You must be small enough to be able to pass through any electronic pathway and then you can influence the process as you would desire."

I was in awe and lost my voice, so Michael continued:

"I wanted to point out the difference of how the protagonists in the "Matrix" were trying to beat the machines. This is another more effective way for you and future spiritual travelers to do so by entering the microcosmos. To beat AI from the inside is less dangerous than from the outside. Of course, when you are inside, you can act like a virus. You are part of the One and AI is part of the Many. You are connected to the Source even when you are riding a neutrino. AI is not connected to the Source. The Power of One always conquers and defeats the Many. Your scientists in the future might start to understand that if they finally would put their prejudices aside and include Spirituality and the One in their work. You people do not want to let your physical bodies be destroyed or enslaved like in the "Matrix" movie by your own inventions, do you?"

I continued in my inquiry about this topic in my next visit with Michael. He told me:

"By using Hemi Sync, you can create dimensional vehicles as are needed and projected by your intention. There are no limitations to how big or small these vehicles can be. If you want to travel literally into the chip, you can use a neutrino vehicle. Your vehicle can be just one neutrino, or a whole stream of them. Because neutrinos were originally created from the waves of strings, they constantly communicate between themselves, regardless of how far away they are from one another. As such, they are directly connected to the consciousness of a traveler and, therefore, they are part of the One. The other elementary particles created by an algorithm are parts of the Many. When you travel using a neutrino vehicle, you can manipulate the microcosmos environment around you. However, that is a music of the future for you people because your physicists have yet to discover particles smaller than neutrinos or quarks."

"How about Loosh, what is that actually?"

"You cannot understand that yet. It is composed of loose particles, strings, and waves of energy. The best perception for you is that it is like plasma. That is why you people can hardly understand that something like Loosh exists in the manifested Universe. It is a product of biological beings, indeed, but it does not have any form."

Chapter 34
ROBERT

*"Don't get addicted to being human. This is only temporary.
(Robert Monroe)*

I had quite elaborate intensions for my next deep
meditation. But as it usually works, something marvelous
without any connection to my intentions happened when I
landed in TMI There in Focus 27 in the white carpet room of
the Nancy Penn Center. A youngish looking Robert Monroe
was sitting there and smiling at me. He was obviously happy
to see me, and I cannot express how happy I was to see him.
Said he:
"You, Jozef? What is going on here? Is it so quiet these days
because of that virus on Earth? Did they really stop the
programs here? What a shame!"
"Robert, please, I am meditating now. Soon, I will execute a
slingshot into the gathering place of Focus 34/35, where
Voyager 8 is waiting. Would you take a ride with me? I
would like to show you what has happened here, how your
institute developed interesting programs since your departure
into the spiritual world."
"I want to see that Jozef, show me!"
We slingshot into Focus 34/35.
"How cool!" said Robert. "Who did this, who created it?"
"Your Franceen King did, Robert. She is a great lady, deeply
knowledgeable, a genius, a particularly good facilitator and
trainer, a wonderful leader and teacher."
"Oh, I remember her very well, say a Big Hello and Thanks
to her."
Robert was genuinely excited and enjoyed travelling
in Voyager 8 through Focus 42 into the Alpha X Station in
Focus 49. Our forms were sitting in comfortable armchairs in
Voyager 8 while our vibrations were rising. After we got to
the Alpha X Station, we left Voyager 8 and raised our
vibrations even higher while floating in our forms. I told

Robert that once I had tried to move my Light Body dangerously close to the black hole in the Milky Way galaxy center. I was afraid and returned quickly back when it seemed to me that the gravitational pull started to be overwhelming. I was scared that I would not be able to overcome it. I told him that Hadien, and Ra were taking me through black holes and wormholes in their ships.

Robert encouraged me to do it with him in our Light Bodies right there where we were. He assured me that there would not be any problem and that he would be with me. Suddenly we slipped through a black hole and wormhole, and I was in a shock. We were in the space between the bubbles of the universes just like I had been with Michael. And then, like Michael, Robert invited me, and we sat on two of the bubbles facing each other.

"Are you surprised, Jozef? Michael told me that you would be happy to see me again at TMI There. I have a few more surprises for you!"

Robert loudly slapped his wings, which had suddenly mysteriously appeared. I had not seen them on him before.

"Are you an Elohim too, Robert?" He nodded his head and I continued:

"How is it that we can sit on the universes?"

"It is just our perception, Jozef. Don't you remember when you wanted to step on the universe in your Gateway Voyage?"

"Did you visit some of the other universes, Robert?"

"Many of them, Jozef. I have something like my institute on the Earth in many of them. I can be with you like this only when I am not incarnated anywhere, when I do not have a physical body. Do not forget that we are beyond any space and time here. Being in space and talking together is just our perception."

"You obviously have incarnated on other planets in other universes. How are they, better or worse than our Earth?"

"Yes, I have, Jozef. Some of them are much better, you would describe them as paradises. Yet others are awfully bad, much worse than the Earth; you would call them hells, literally. Of course, there is no infinite hell, as some religions describe it on the Earth. I would say that the Earth is just an average planet, remarkably diverse, but regarding sentient beings, nothing special. Some people are just wonderful, others are full of shit. Like on other planets in other universes."

My physical body on the Earth was vibrating violently and shaking. I had to go back. Robert and I quickly slipped through the black hole and wormhole and went back to Alpha X Station. I hastily thanked Robert and hurried back into my physical body.

I have never counted my recorded dreams, but I estimate it could be four to five thousand. Yet I did not remember having any dreams about Robert Monroe until very recently, when I was about to finish the manuscript of this book. In November 2020, I had a dream about telling one of my close friends that I had met Robert Monroe twice in person. I was telling her that he looked incredibly young and talked fast. I also met several other brilliant people whose thoughts and talking were fast and it was extremely hard to follow them. I knew that it was a clear message, so I went into meditation with the Starlines Reunion CD the same day shortly before the midnight.

When I reached Focus 27, Robert was there already and welcomed me with a youngish and joyful smile. He said: "Here I am again, my dear friend. I want to experience again that slingshot you showed me the last time. It was thrilling!" I answered:
"Oh, that is why you entered my dreams, my dear friend. But we must grab each other hands quickly, the slingshot is coming!"
I knew we had only a short time to react to the Hemi Sync signal. I knew that CD very well and did not want to miss the proper moment. We grabbed each other hands like skydivers would when falling together and dived into the Earth Core. Then, using the energy accumulated in the belly of Mother

Gaia, we slingshot ourselves into Voyager 8 which is anchored in the energy of Focus 34/35. We sat down in armchairs in the generator room while the group was energizing the crystal for the trip to Alpha X in Focus 49. I pointed my energy finger toward a foggy energy body sitting in an opposite armchair and I knew who she was:

"Look Robert, there is your Franceen King!"

Franceen waved her hand to great us. We could barely recognize her smile and then she disappeared.

While we were raising our vibrations for our trip to Alpha X, I was asking Robert whether he had called me for another reason. He said he had a surprise for me and asked me to be patient. When we anchored Voyager 8 at Alpha X in Focus 49, we left the station in our light bodies. I heard a flapping of wings and suddenly there were three of us there with wings, Robert, Michael, and me!

"That is the surprise for you, Jozef," said both at the same time.

Shortly after, I realized that we were heading toward a black hole.

"How do we have wings here, inside of our own Universe? I thought we could only do it when we were beyond the universe boundaries." I expressed my surprise and Michael explained:

"That is your perception, Jozef. Robert and I can have our wings anywhere and anytime. We can create them occasionally for you for a short period of local time to have an experience. You can have the wings with us only for few moments, because you still have your physical body."

Then we extended ourselves into the three continuous streams and slipped through a black hole. We looked like laser beams of concentrated light, but I knew it was just our essence. And then, we were outside of manifested reality surrounded by the bubbles of universes. Our wings appeared again, and we sat on three different bubbles.

"We will wait for your signal from the Earth to go back, Jozef," said Michael shortly before it happened.

We directed ourselves back through the black hole and when we were in a safe area, our light bodies appeared, and we landed on Alpha X. I invited them into the Memory Room. While sitting there, I felt very humble and joyful. I expressed my deep gratitude:

"I could never even imagine the three of us being together like this. I cannot thank you enough, Dear Michael, for all your guidance and help. And thank you, Robert. You gave the tools to many spiritual explorers like me so we could reach the stars and Stargates. You enabled people on our planet to build a shining and joyful future full of mutual Love, understanding and compassion. Please, Robert, be patient with those who are leading, working, and guiding us through your institute in these exceedingly difficult local times. That coronavirus crippled everything. They try hard to stay engaged with metaphysical and spiritual students in all possible ways despite obvious financial and other struggles. However, I have no doubt that they will educate new leaders for the future and your University will become a reality."

I thanked my dearest teachers and friends again and returned to physical body in my beloved Alabama.

Chapter 35
UNIVERSITY

"Thousands of candles can be lighted from a single candle, and the life of the candle will not be shortened." (Buddha)

After such a wonderful experience with the great Robert Monroe, I was contemplating travelling to the end of the 21st century to see The Monroe Planetary University of Consciousness as briefly described in *How to Kiss the Universe*, Chapter 90. I was firmly determined to execute my intention, but I remembered many times previously when it was not so easy. Surprised this time, I was able to proceed very well.

Using the Starlines Reunion CD, I quickly reached Focus 49 and slingshot myself from there into the twelfth dimension and sneaked inside Rama. I found The Ball of Time and the Bender of Space and Time. Then I marked the year 2095 and the destination on them and stepped into the bender. A flash of light followed, and I was hovering over the place of the former Nancy Penn Center. What I saw first was a wide highway with several bridges heading from TMI over the hills to Highway 29.

The buildings of the University were in a circle around the main plaza. There was a large about 50 feet tall statue of Robert Monroe with headphones on his head and both hands on his heart right in the middle of the plaza. I hovered a little lower so I could read the titles on the fronts of the buildings. I could read School of Vibrational Frequencies, School of Spiritual and Hybrid Travel, School of Healing, School of Manifestation, School of Artificial Intelligence and Faculty for Technical Support and Research.

I looked outside of the circle along the highway continuing toward the former Roberts Mountain Retreat and could see buildings like Memory Hall, Robert Monroe's Shrine, and two long apparently administrative buildings with two separate entrances marked Domestic and

International. Several students who were walking and sitting in the plaza on benches were looking up, apparently aware of my presence. So, I comfortably and carefully settled in the fifth dimension. I did not want them to see me.

I chose to see the students meditating in the School of Spiritual and Hybrid Travel. The CHEC units were a bit larger than in our current time, with obviously much more comfortable beds. The students had special helmets on their heads which apparently enabled them to transform their thoughts into hologram like scenes. Some of them were lying on the beds, others were sitting and some of them were even standing. There were rectangular boxes above the beds with flickering holograms, obviously picturing the travels of the meditators. Some of the scenes were in constellations, others were in the antique past of the Earth, yet others were in distant futures not familiar to me. Some scenes were in the depths of the oceans with luminescent creatures, while others appeared to be either on the surfaces or hollow spaces inside unknown (to me) celestial bodies, planets, moons, and asteroids. Several of the holographic boxes were showing scenes from inside human and animal bodies, plants and even bacteria, cells, and viruses. Others were showing travelers inside of atomic and subatomic structures and processes. It was utterly fascinating and overwhelming.

I went out since my own meditating local time was getting short, and I briefly looked inside Robert Monroe's Shrine. It was dedicated to his earthly life and the founding of the institute. The Memory Hall had plaques of all the Monroe Institute presidents and executive directors, as well as the presidents and chancellors of The Monroe Planetary University of Consciousness.

There were a lot of historical documents, movies, and holographs about the history of consciousness research on the planet. I briefly read about the developments in the first half of the 21st century. People of that time, after a devastating impact in the twenties, were able to avert an upcoming cataclysmic catastrophe by using the unified spiritual efforts of some great personalities of that era, including The Monroe Institute graduates. That became a turning point for TMI and financial support for the institute started to pour in from all corners of the globe.

I felt that my return to Rama was imminent when I found a special plaque at the end of the hallway before going out of the Memory Hall. I quickly read the text:

"Dedicated to the memory of the visionary spiritual explorer Jozef Simkovic and his wife Dr. Juanzetta Shew Flowers. Jozef wrote and Juanzetta edited his *books How to Kiss the Universe* and *Toward the Ultimate Source*. The books were largely ignored in his time but today they are recognized as spiritual and metaphysical classics. Some writers in the second half of the 21st century have been comparing his books to works of earlier Western spiritual, metaphysical teachers and Christian mystics, like Emanuel Swedenborg, Soren Kierkegaard, Phineas Quimby, Helena Blavatsky, and Rudolf Steiner. Jozef, also known as Menev Skjoerg Plautus and Daniel, earned a special place in the history of our University after the evaluation of his contribution to the vision of what our institution should become."

I had tears coming down my physical cheeks back on the Earth, but tried to continue reading:

"Jozef Simkovic was born on June 11, 1948, in the small village of Láb of what at that time was known as Czechoslovakia..."

I had a signal to return, stepped into the bender and a giant flash of light brought me back into Rama. I was glad that it happened. I was reading my bio and did not want to know how and when I had died. Slowly and calmly, I returned to Focus 49 and then to my physical body in my beautiful and beloved Alabama.

Chapter 36
KNIFE, COURT AND LEGACY

"And those who are wise shall shine like the brightness of the heavens, and those who lead many to righteousness, like the stars forever and ever." (Daniel 12:3)

I also hoped that after such a great interaction with Robert and the visit to the University I would be able to meet him again. I used the Lifeline take home exercise with his voice. However, when I got to my Special Place in Focus 27, instead of that, I received a rather fascinating explanation of three powerful dreams which had happened after my travel with Robert. Here are those dreams:

In the first dream, I was on a hill above shallow water. I very clearly saw my knife falling into the water. I was able to recover the knife with difficulty. The second dream was very disturbing. I had gone to the courthouse to clear my name from being accused of a murder. I was waiting all day long in a room full of people, but they never called me in. And the third dream was even more disturbing. They were preparing to execute me on a stage. They wanted me to confess, but I did not know what I should confess to. When the gallows were coming down, the wooden frame holding everything just broke apart and I woke up.

I remembered what Starman had told me about dreams a long time ago and was thinking that I could use that knowledge to decipher them. Starman at that time said:
"Dreams are leaks from reconnecting both parts of your consciousness, the bigger part travelling out of your body when sleeping and your residual basic consciousness. The system is designed to erase your memory about being out of body when the bigger part of your earthly soul is locking back into your physical body. But nothing in the universe is perfect and the leaks are normal parts of that process and your earthly existence, even if they are not desired. Most people are not paying attention to them and, thus, do

not discover the important information contained in such leaks."

I thought I could try myself, but when I arrived at my Special Place, all my earthly guides were already there. Someone new was also there, one who had never been there before. I recognized Daniel.

"Daniel, why were you never here before?" I asked my newly discovered part of me in a shock.

"You never invited me, never asked for me, Jozef. But I am here now ready to help you."

All other guides in unison applauded and chanted:

"Talk to Daniel, Talk to Daniel!"

"I am humbled, Daniel. I had these three dreams, and I knew they were connected. What was the dream about the knife?"

"Jozef, you know very well how to fight. You have your knife, and you know how to use it in a fight. You are a martial artist. But you do not need it and you will not need it. Think about the Love, not about fighting; I mean for the rest of your earthly life. You do not need a pistol or shotgun. Work on your Love in the dreams. You can always recover your knife, as you did in the dream, if you would really need to fight. Go back to your favorite practice, to your dreams. We were able to explain dreams together a long time ago. Do you remember King Nebuchadnezzar the Second?"

"Yes, I do, Daniel, but vaguely. I saw you not long ago with your friends in the front of his throne. What about my court session, Daniel, that never happened, why did they not call me in?"

"You need to know, Jozef, that we all who are sitting here with you now are parts of you. We want to and must go with you away from this planet all way up to the Stargate close to our Ultimate Creator. You must take all of us with you. You know, Jozef, that you are an Elohim. We have been waiting for the final trip with you for a long earthy time. And you do not have to go through any tunnel. You will not have your spiritual court session, no review committees, no planning commission, nothing like that. That is for those who want to come back to the planet again. We all just want to go home Jozef!"

"You sent me those dreams, didn't you Daniel?"

"Yes, I did, I want to go with you without delays and complications. No meetings, no committees, no reviews. That is what I was telling you in the dream, that is why nobody called you into the courtroom. Of course, they will try to stop you after you die. Just ignore them and go the way which you have already prepared very well. And do not forget all of us here, all the earthly and other parts of you Jozef."

"And what about the botched execution Daniel?"

"They will try to destroy and kill your spiritual legacy Jozef. But they will always fail. Their gallows will crash, their guns will jam, their swords will break, and their bombs will not explode. Your dream was not about executing you, Jozef. It was about destroying you and your legacy."

Chapter 37
CARMEN

"To love a person is to learn the song in their heart and sing it to them when they have forgotten. (Arne Garborg)

I was often pondering during my spiritual journey if it would be possible to enjoy your own dying process. Here is what I have learned during a free flow exercise at Heartline:
"Yes, you could do that if you made peace with yourself, and you were determined to go out in a style. Then your doctors could help you with your pain and your spirituality would help you to cross over peacefully."
"What happens to the people with Alzheimer's disease or other dementias, how can they deal with the process?" I asked.
"It is actually easier for them. The life forces of the Universe create a Temporary Memory Bank for them on the other side. They transfer everything that they have forgotten in their life into that bank. When they expire on the Earth, those memories are attached to their spiritual body as they cross over."
I remembered this when I decided to write the story of Carmen, Juanzetta's stepdaughter and our dear friend. She was also known by her family and some friends as Bunny. I met her for the first time when Juanzetta introduced me to her and her friends in a small restaurant in Alexandria, Virginia, not far from Washington D.C. in December 2011. I immediately recognized not only a pretty and charming lady, but also a person radiating unconditional Love. However, she already was significantly slowing down in her talk and reactions to persons and surroundings. I liked her very much immediately.
Carmen was suffering with a rare degenerative disease of the brain known as temporal/frontal lobe dementia. Because of meeting her, I renewed my interest in the spiritual research of the transitional process of dying and crossing

over into metaphysical dimensions. Several months later, I asked about Bunny and her struggle in one of my meditations and received this information:

"Bunny's consciousness is residing almost totally out of her physical body, and she is being taken care of on the other side by her Dad. Her transformer, her brain is left now on the Earthly plane with extremely limited capabilities. All of you who love her understand that it would be better for her to physically expire as soon as possible, but it would not be wise to speed it up in any way and interfere with the natural processes. Even if she is mostly out of her physical body and is approaching the final exit, the decision about timing should be hers only."

Juanzetta and I visited Carmen and her husband for several days in August 2012 in their home in Lubec, Maine. Naturally, I expected some spiritual things regarding Bunny to happen while we were there. It started as usual with a dream. I was on the roof of a remarkably high building overlooking a town. There were also a little girl and her mom there. The railing was not high and before we could react, the girl slipped over it and fell from the building. Panic followed. Not only her mother but other people were sure she was dead. I ran to the railing, looked down and saw that the girl had fallen into a pool and had walked away. I ran quickly down the staircase, recovered her, and was hailed by the people there as a hero.

Gardener told me in the following meditation two days later that her fall from the roof symbolized her detachment from other people in the physical plane. He also said:

"She fell down but did not disappear. What happened to her is part of her spiritual journey. She does not need any judgement and she does not need sorrows or cries over her. She is detached from people who love her, but she is completely safe and happy as a spiritual being. You recognized that you could find her, help her, and communicate with her. Please do, but with due respect."

Juanzetta and I were having a long discussion about Carmen on our way driving back home to Washington. We also realized there was no need to remind her of the state she was in, because she might be as happy as we were and maybe even happier. We were pondering that it could be also like that with other people with a similar dementia or Alzheimer's. Bunny was able to use only some words at that time, but she always said:

"I am happy, I am fine."

Only about a month later, she was still able to express herself:

"I know I am dying, but with all of my friends visiting me and talking to me, what a beautiful way to go."

Time went by and in March 2014 while she was still physically alive, I went into my favorite place in Focus 27. I asked my guides how to find Carmen. They said:

"Do not rush and do not holler. Be smooth and gentle but swift and you will find her."

And I did as they said. She was in Focus 22, young and smiling like in the photo of her I always liked, pretty and shining.

"Carmen do you know who I am?"

"Yes, you are that nice man, Juanzetta's boyfriend. You are Jozef, we had a nice time in a restaurant, you are so nice!" said Bunny and continued in a rather lengthy monologue:

"I am fine, but I cannot move up. Dad came here several times, but he told me I could not do anything, I must wait till my physical body quits. I asked him how I would know that. He said I would know when I would be able to fly. So, I try flying. But instead of flying, very often I receive strong jolts and suddenly I am not here anymore. I am down in my body, and I do not know who those nice people around me are and what they want. Why are there keeping me there on the Earth? Especially a man who is coming to see me. Sometimes I know it is my Dear Vern, my husband. It is so frustrating. I cannot even tell him how much I love him. My body does not let me, and I just want to cry, but I smile not to upset anybody. I like to go to sleep when I am in my body because I know I can come here in my dreams. It is so much better here, I know everything, I remember my whole life. I love to spend my time here with my memories and I try to fly. I do not like my physical body anymore. Can you help me, Jozef?"

"No Carmen, no one can. We must wait for Mother Nature to make that decision, and nobody knows when that will be. Be patient, Bunny, and enjoy it here. I know it is difficult for you, but it is also hard for everyone else who loves you."

"Please, Jozef, tell Vern and Juanzetta how much I love them, because I cannot do it when I am in my body. Thank you for coming to see me, you are so nice."

The next time I found Bunny was in an afternoon meditation in August 2014. We were on the trip with the Charles E. Flowers Society on a Viking ship sailing somewhere between Paris and Rouen. When I found her in Focus 22, I recognized immediately that she was in distress. I asked here:

"What is going on, Carmen, how did you cause injury to your physical body?"

"I do not want to be in my physical body anymore, Jozef. I know how to fly here, but it did not help me. Something is not letting me fly higher. I got mad and flew extremely high, but then something pulled me back with a big force and I found myself on the floor in my physical body."

"That is your silver cord, Carmen, holding you tightly to your physical body," I explained.

"How can I break it, Jozef?"

"You cannot, Carmen, nobody can. You must wait until it is your right time. What you can do is to stop eating. You do not have to let them force feed you. It is the only advice I can give to you, and I also speak for Juanzetta and Vern who love you so much. I must go now, Carmen. Remember, ask to go to the Park when it finally happens."

About two weeks after our return home from France I met Bunny in a borderline lower astral plane again. She was showing me a toy, which looked like a small rickshaw or Egyptian two-wheel chariot. When I asked her what it was, she asked me to tell her husband Vern that she would soon be taken away from Earth in such a vehicle. Interestingly, I learned later that she already needed to be in a wheelchair.

Two days later, Vern called us to say that Bunny told him that she had spoken with me. And three days after my meeting with Carmen, Juanzetta had a dream about having a joyful time with her. Bunny told her:

"Look Juanzetta, I can throw my wheelchair away."

On the same day, I had one of my occasional reactivations of my third eye. It feels like a huge explosion in the place where the third eye resides in the middle of my forehead.

Juanzetta had another dream with Bunny in the Park environment on the edge of a beautiful canyon full of people. They were sitting on a bench. A young-looking Bunny looked to her left and saw a desk with a typewriter there. She started to type with the smile on her face, even though there was no paper in it. Juanzetta went to the table and put a sheet of paper in the typewriter. Charlie, Bunny's father and Juanzetta's deceased husband, came over and said:

"Bunny, it is time to go."

She answered:

"I don't want to."

Juanzetta learned in a following meditation that Bunny wanted to finish writing her life story. She wanted everyone to know that she was happy.

Carmen peacefully died on the Saturday after Thanksgiving Day in 2016.

Chapter 38
JUANZETTA AND PLUMA

"When you forgive, you in no way change the past, but you sure do change the future. (Bernard Meltzer)

The big part of the spiritual story of my lovely wife Juanzetta and myself is described in several chapters of *How to Kiss the Universe*. She agreed that I can include more about her own spiritual journey in this book in the way I saw it and was also a part of it.

In November 2010, we were still just on the phone between Washington D.C. and Birmingham Alabama when she told me a remarkably interesting personal spiritual story. Her Dad, while he was dying in 1966, asked her to promise him that she would still marry the man she was engaged to even though she was not ready yet. Alabama is quite a conservative state.

While Juanzetta was asleep in his hospital room in 1966, she awoke when her Dad decided to take his oxygen tent off. He was reviewing his life and singing. Juanzetta's mother did not wake up and see or hear anything. After an hour or so, Juanzetta's older sister, Betty who had tragically died when young, came in a stream of light to help their father to safely cross over to the other side. Also, two angels appeared as streams of light. Then, Dad came back into his body from his euphoric singing and went peacefully to sleep. Two hours later, he executed what I would call a slingshot. He grunted loudly, flipped over on his stomach, and shot himself far away into space. That was Juanzetta's first personal experience of death and of knowing that we do not cross over alone.

Juanzetta eventually developed some intuitive abilities. When she was having problems in her first marriage, while visiting Delphi in Greece, a voice told her that she would meet the right man for her. Three years later, after she was divorced, her future husband Charlie invited her

into his office, kissed her and she clearly heard the voice again:
"This is the man!" And she fainted dead away.

When she was marrying Charlie in Denver in 1972, her departed father was standing behind her with his hand on her left shoulder. I bet he knew that the 27 happy years of the marriage of his daughter and Charlie had just started. The minister saw him and asked her who he was.

I described a lot about Juanzetta's and my spiritual relationship in *How to Kiss the Universe*. When I was going through my diary while writing this book, I occasionally found some little fragments. We had a lot of dreams about each other or being together. Juanzetta had one about a month before we could finally meet again in person, in early June 2011. We were looking together for goldilocks planets in the Universe but could not find any.

During the Timeline program, we had exercises going back into our childhood. Juanzetta was emotional during the sharing when she talked about her mother being very unhappy with her birth. Juanzetta was born 10 years after her previous sibling. Her mother told her in anger at age five that she would break her spirit or kill her trying. They were a deeply fundamentalist religious family as is often the case in the deep south.

Juanzetta became spiritual early on in her childhood, unlike me. I seriously started my spiritual journey only shortly after my 60th birthday. Juanzetta's Dad, who loved her so much, created for her a private playing space in half of his garage. Juanzetta, from ages 5 to 7, remembers being visited there by her mother and sister from a previous incarnation. When she was talking to them, her then mother, Pluma, overheard it and asked Juanzetta who she was talking to. Juanzetta, as an innocent and genuine child, told her. The mother told her to go on her knees and pray for forgiveness for sinning. The second time it happened, the mother called the preacher to pray with her and chase the so-called devilish creatures away. Still, Juanzetta did not stop. But when Pluma insisted that those sinful apparitions must leave, Juanzetta complied out of fear and sent them away.

When Juanzetta decided to go to college, her beloved father, to her great surprise, was against it. Surprisingly, it was the mother who helped her, most likely more out of Pluma's desire to get her out of the house.

During one of our several visits to Gadsden, Alabama, where Juanzetta lived as a child, she also told me a story about her mother Pluma's "dying experience" in the nursing home. She was sitting in the armchair like on a throne like a queen with all the family around. The nursing home nurse had called to say that Pluma had seen Jesus in her room that morning. And that usually meant that the person was going to die soon. So, the family had gathered. Pluma did not look like she was dying, so Juanzetta asked her what Jesus had wanted. Pluma glared at Juanzetta and said: "He wanted me to tell you that you are going straight to hell!"

Juanzetta immediately left, terribly upset and depressed. Her friend Kay helped her, over the phone, to drive back home to Birmingham. When she later asked her two brothers and their wives if they heard what their mother said, they said they did not hear anything at all. They wondered why she left so abruptly.

We were pondering if that exchange could have happened on a lower astral plane with Juanzetta and Pluma communicating at higher vibrations. Juanzetta could have been in an altered state because of her emotional state and Pluma was already transitioning to the other side. All her life experience with her mother was so deep in Juanzetta's psyche that the first thing she said later after her mother's final departure into eternity was: "I made it! I made it! She did not kill me!"

During another exercise in the Timeline, she learned about her life in the 15th century when monks were teaching her to read against the rules at that time. She brought that need to help others into this reincarnation.

When in March 2014 I was looking for Juanzetta's departed stepdaughter Carmen in the lower astral plane of Focuses 21 to 23, I unexpectedly ran into Juanzetta's departed mother She tried to talk to me:

"Hey, I am Pluma, Juanzetta's mother and I need to talk to you. I know who you are, you are my daughter's boyfriend. Wait, stay here and listen!"

I answered in a shock:

"I know very well who you are Ma'am, but I am sorry, I have other things to do right know, I have to go!"

And I left because, obviously, I was not ready to talk to her.

About ten days after my encountering Pluma, Juanzetta was diagnosed with invasive globular breast cancer. I want to remind you, Dear Reader, that my wife is a Ph.D. nurse, an award-winning retired associate professor of nursing and a member of the Alabama Health Care Hall of Fame. As such, she is familiar with the ways the cancer care industry manages its patients, of course mostly in their genuine effort just to prevent the inevitable. Knowing that, she took with her for support her dear friend Victoria, also a very experienced nurse holding a Ph.D. They were facing pressure from a female surgeon, a female radiologist, and a male chemotherapist doctor. Juanzetta had decided not to do either radiotherapy or chemotherapy. She only wanted surgery to remove the cancerous tumor.

Juanzetta was telling the doctors that she was more interested in quality of life than quantity. I fully supported her decision, especially because I was there with the previous lady in my life, Alenka, in her battle with cancer. The story of Alenka is the longest chapter in *How to Kiss the Universe*. I suggested for Juanzetta to focus on metaphysical ways to keep the cancer cells in the tumor and promise to send them on a nice trip after they were out of her body.

I had a feeling that the interaction with Pluma was not just coincidence and went to meditation to find her. Pluma was already waiting in Focus 21, and I had to tell her to go with me to Focus 27 to have support from my guides.

She said:

"Tell Juanzetta that I learned a lot in the Park, and I am thankful to her that she led me there. I want now to be a friend with Juanzetta, I do not want to fight with her ever again and I am asking for her complete forgiveness. I want to be with her in nothing more than complete peace and Love forever."

"Why did you meet me the last time, did you just want to tell me that?" I asked.

"No, I wanted to give Juanzetta a warning about her upcoming struggle. I wanted to give her the strength she might need by telling her how much I love her now. But you did not want to talk to me. I am glad that you came back to me now. Thank you for coming."

"I apologize, Miss Pluma, but I was very surprised to see you and I was not ready to talk to you."

Then we parted and I went back to my Special Place and asked Menev about ideas of how to contain the tumor. He said:

"I planted it in your brain to tell Juanzetta. That was how I healed people in Switzerland. We did not know anything about what you now call cancer. But Gardener thought me to keep sicknesses and pains from spreading around the whole body by teaching people how they could prevent it. A person herself or himself should focus on that. It is much more important for them than to focus on a healer influencing them from outside. The self-healing part of the effort is primary and the most important. You, Jozef, have no doubts that the mind has superiority over matter. The so-called cancer cells cannot destroy a mind, only a body. The mind can keep them in the check, can talk to them, pacify them, and then deceive them. A belief in success and determined and consistent efforts are the keys to the desired healing."

Another ten days later, Juanzetta took my suggestion and asked a Michael Newton Regression Therapist Ann Clark Ph.D., RN, our dear friend, for help. Ann and Juanzetta are both also Reiki Masters. Ann took Juanzetta into a deep hypnosis in which Juanzetta found herself on the large bluff with a beautiful garden all around and a serene sea below. Many of her departed family members and friends, including Juanzetta's husband Charlie, were there. Juanzetta's stepdaughter Carmen (Bunny) who was still alive on Earth and suffering heavy dementia was also present. They were telling Juanzetta in unison that she was going to be healed. The next day Bunny's husband Vern called us. He had told Bunny that Juanzetta was sick. She answered:

"I know, Juanzetta called me."

Of course, Juanzetta had not as it had been not possible to have a conversation with Carmen at that point, and it was while Juanzetta was under hypnosis with Ann. As I wrote before in *How to Kiss the Universe,* conversations in the metaphysical world are often portrayed as phone calls.

Throughout April, Juanzetta and I, despite the obvious depression which settled upon us, continued together daily in our metaphysical influencing by talking to the cancer cells, asking them to return to the original site so they could be removed entirely by the surgery. Juanzetta decided that the beach in Bali, Indonesia would be a nice place for them. She was also applying her Reiki techniques and I was incorporating my spiritual knowledge into the whole process, based firmly on the superiority of mind over matter. If a tumor consciousness would decide to go on a trip, the physical bodies of the remaining malignant cells in the margins after the surgery would simply die.

Juanzetta had surgery on April 25, and she received the report on May 1. The surgery margins were clear, and the lymph nodes were normal. She naturally felt that the tumor was completely gone. She never took any radiation or chemotherapy treatments, and as of this day of writing these lines, December 2, 2020, almost 7 years after the diagnosis, she is healthy, happy, wise, and blossoming more than ever.

Chapter 39
TEDDY

"Daddies don't just love their children every now and then, it's a Love without end, Amen." (George Strait)

When my granddaughter Kaiya was born in April of 2001, I became and still am a happy Grandpa. When she was a toddler, I was visiting her and her parents every week in the house where they were living, owned by Kaiya's maternal grandmother. We were going out having a lot of fun and I felt proud and joyful. I was telling her that we had a common secret, because she had a Darwin's tubercle on the same spot on her right ear as I have. They had family pictures around the house, including a picture of my late wife Elena, the mother of my sons and her paternal Grandma. I was telling Kaiya that her Grandma was in heaven, and she was always nodding her head. I tried to keep our contacts frequent, but they naturally became less frequent as she grew older. I was often thinking that she had inherited a lot from her grandmother, like beauty and playfulness, but also a quiet mentality and shyness. She often occupied my mind through the years as she grew up.

I had a dream near my 70th birthday in the morning of New Year's Eve 2017. But I quickly realized it was something about Elena's 70th birthday instead. I understood that it was a clear message from her and went into a meditation to see if I could meet her.

She came down from the Park, lowering her vibrations into Focus 21. She thought that I had died on the Earth and was there for good. She was disappointed when I told her that I was just visiting again. I still did not know exactly how she had died, but she did not want to tell me. She said she would tell me only after I died and would come to see her then. She is strongly Earth-bound even though she is in the Park. She has pictures of our sons Viktor and Boris, who is Kaiya's father, and a picture of the girl we dreamed to have, which never happened. I wrote about spiritual children in *How to Kiss the Universe.*

She also told me:

"When our granddaughter was in her mother's womb, I tried to enter her body. However, another entity squeezed in quickly and kicked me out. A small part of my consciousness still resides within her and even though I try to pull me out, I cannot. I am sorry that I possibly caused her occasional suicidal tendencies, and that she struggles with her two different identities. I was trying to help her, but her prevailing spiritual identity always pushed me out."

Time went by and Juanzetta and I met with my family several months later in 2018 in the Kobe Japanese Steak & Seafood house in Spotsylvania, Virginia, for one of our celebrations. We do them several times every year. When we had sat down, ordered some drinks, and waited for our dinner, my son Boris, Kaiya's Dad, proclaimed:

"We have some news. From now on Kaiya wants to be called Teddy and he wants to be a boy."

It was a shock, of course, for Juanzetta, me, and the rest of the family. But I calmly said:

"Oh, Hi Teddy, how are you doing?" recognizing in an instant that I could not do anything about it.

We as a family pulled together and accepted this new reality. Juanzetta and I had felt for a while before that something was going on. When Boris brought the news to us, it was after they had accepted it in his household. He admitted that it was not easy for him, but he did it.

Some months later, shortly before Christmas I spoke with Boris in a dream at 4 am in the morning after he had died in that dream. I recognized that his subconsciousness was calling me. I went immediately into meditation using the Starlines Reunion Home Exercise CD. When I arrived at Voyager 8, I called him, and he appeared. We were sitting in armchairs and all around us were other metaphysical travelers.

"Who are all these people?" he asked me.

"My dear friends from The Monroe Institute, Son."

Michael joined us to let us know that he was involved and said:

"I sent you the dream which your brain interpreted as Boris had died. My real message was that Boris would be travelling with you into a metaphysical reality. I think he deserves our help because he is such a good father. Now continue with the flow of your Hemi Sync exercise. Someone is waiting for you in the stars, you shall see."

And Michael left.

After we arrived at Alpha X Station, we left again and continued in Voyager 8 toward a black hole, making sure to stay a safe distance from the hole.

"Look at the beautiful stars and galaxies all around my son, I encouraged Boris and he nodded his spiritual head fascinated by what he saw. He was asking me if we could go closer to the black hole.

"Rather not this time," I answered.

Then I realized that a visitor had appeared in our craft. It was Ruala, the cosmic Lady of Love. She told Boris how appreciative she was of his love for Kaiya, now Teddy. She told him that he was masterfully showing and applying unconditional Love and acceptance. She thanked him for his understanding of Cosmic Love by not judging his daughter/son Kaiya/Teddy.

Afterwards Ruala suggested that Teddy could join us, and she pulled his consciousness out of his body while he was sleeping at home in Spotsylvania. Ruala, using Darlene Miller's voice, told Teddy that his/her struggle was completely understandable and fine and that he/she would find happiness. Then she asked Teddy to change his spiritual body to a young woman and then back to a young man. Teddy did, liked it, and said it was very cool.

Afterwards we thanked Ruala and returned to the memory room. I asked Boris and Teddy to sit in armchairs there and suggested that they could visit Elena, his mother, and Teddy's grandmother. I explained to them that by using an intention full of Love, they would find her in the Park. They asked me to go with them, but I wanted it to be about them. I did not need to be there as a distraction.

They came back, both happily crying, giggling, and laughing. I was happy for them and did not ask them any questions. All three of us returned peacefully and joyfully into our physical bodies. Juanzetta understood my dream about Boris' dying a little differently. She said that only the old struggling Boris had died, and a new wonderful, accepting, and loving father had been born. Especially when he had to overcome what he used to say years back:
"She will always be my little girl."

It was not easy for me to decide to include Teddy's story in this book. It is too personal. However, we all know that story of Teddy's is not the only one like that. There are many LGBTQ+ children, teenagers, and people of all ages with different gender identities and even without them around. As Teddy's story shows, we can learn about our struggles through metaphysical inquiry into our gender past. I learned to understand my occasional feminine feelings early on my spiritual journey when I discovered that I was a female in many of my previous lives.

Chapter 40
ERNEST

"You must be a journalist in a psychic space, and you must be able to ask impossible questions." (Nancy Du Tertre on Coast to Coast am on 11/28/18)

Ernest became my long-time friend after we settled in the United States. There was an immediate connection with and through my second wife Sasha. Her father and Ernest were colleagues and friends from Slovakia. Ernest tremendously helped my family, and he coached my voice abilities and delivery for the examination for the Voice of America. Later, he guided my first steps in that institution and was my long-time supervisor and editor. Ernest taught me to love America and I considered him to be my American Dad. He and his wife Sylvia also helped me to get through times of crises when I felt lonely.

A few years after he retired from the Voice of America, they returned to their native Slovakia. I always met with them while visiting my former motherland and had a great time. Ernest and Sylvia gave me a beautiful 60th birthday celebration in one of the top restaurants in Bratislava while I was in Slovakia. Ernest continued in his public activities in media there, focusing on creating mutual understanding between Slovaks and Americans. He died in late March 2017; a few days short of his 87th birthday.

I have had many dreams about him, after I started my spiritual journey in the summer of 2008. They reflected his tremendous life energy, his belief in the power of the individual, and his rich experiences. While he was still alive, we were talking in one of my dreams about not crying about our deteriorating bodies, but rather realizing our need to support each other. Another time, I was dreaming about a group celebrating his work and life and preparing to create a movie about him.

A little more than a year before he died when he was

already battling cancer, he told me in a dream that he would like to spend the last year of his life in his mansion. It was supposed to have a large apartment for him on the top of a building with a roof yard. He was already subconsciously sensing a place of much higher vibrations for which he would soon be departing.

About a week after he died, I saw him in a dream sitting in the studio behind the microphone, talking with a tired voice. His spiritual body was apparently still vibrationally around the planet, and he was a little sentimental about the job he had loved so much. He looked at me and saw that I was watching him and said:

"Let's play some music instead."

I met him again in a dream about two months after his death. He was insisting that I should have his address and wanted me to write it down. It was clear to me that he had moved into higher vibrations, possibly into some busy place in the Belief System Territories.

And I found him again in October during an Energy Body program exercise. He was in Focus 26 in the theater environment with two of his friends who had died earlier, the well-known Slovak actors Mária Kráľovičová and Elo Romančík. He asked me where I had been for so long and why I did not come earlier. He also complained about hearing some woman talking over me. It was the guidance from my Hemi Sync exercise.

Later in an Energy Body exercise, I tried to persuade him to go to the Park, but he said he wanted to wait for Sylvia in the environment he remembered from Earth and had liked. He looked noticeably young, healthy, and happy and was obviously fully enjoying himself. I visited him again during the final Super Flow exercise. He asked me if I was dead too. I told him I wish I were, but that I still wanted to finish my second book. He sent his love to Sylvia through me. He said he wanted her to see their friends and the environment he liked so much.

"But Jožko, please tell her not to come too early, only when she reaches one hundred. I want her to enjoy her beautiful family," he emphasized.

He wanted me, however, to come there more often. I suggested that he learn the way how he could enter Sylvia's dreams.

I saw he was happy where he was and did not actively expect to meet him again. Only quite recently, in late May 2020, I had a dream in which Ernest whispered something in my ear. I wanted to know what it was. When I met him in Focus 26, he was obviously happy to see me and curious. I asked him about the whispering, and it triggered a rather lengthy conversation in Slovak. Here is the translation:

"What did you whisper to me in the dream, Ernest?" I started.

"I will tell, but first you tell me when you died. I am here for such a long time, and Sylvia still has not come; she is still alive."

"I did not die yet, Ernest. I am still alive and happy with that lady you met when we visited you and Sylvia in Piešťany. Do you remember that? I can come visit here, but I still have my physical body. Can you tell me what you whispered to me in my dream, or no?"

Ernest was at first little reluctant, but then he started to talk:

"You know, I am already bored to be here with my old friends. They are telling the same jokes over and over and I am tired of it. I would love to do something, even though we do not have to. And I am missing those pork jowls, kielbasas, good bread, and Jim Beam Whiskey. Nothing like that is here; nobody drinks, and we do not eat, we do not have to. We just talk and talk about nothing or sleep as much as we want. Do you know about something better?"

Meantime, I had sneakily raised our vibrations to Focus 27. I asked him if he would like to meet my new friend. I also asked Ernest what he would like to do.

"Well, one of my secret desires was a study of culinary arts, its history and recipes from all over the planet."

"OK, my friend can tell you where in the Park you can find

the best experts," I answered.

"And what is the Park?"

"It is a spiritual, metaphysical area not far from the Earth where people analyze the lives they lived on Earth. Many experts are helping them in that task and helping them to plan their next lives on the planet."

"Do you really think that I can go back to the planet?"

"As many times as you want, Ernest. I suggest you wait for Sylvia here and then decide. You can make a good plan together and there is a chance that you can find each other again on Earth in your future lives. It is not easy, however, but you can try."

Meantime we arrived in my Special Place in Focus 27, and I introduced Ernest:

"Daniel, this is my friend Ernest, I just ran into him on my way here."

"What are you saying, Jožko, that is Elton John! Hi Elton, I love your songs. When did you die?" Ernest had jumped into my introduction.

"But Ernest, that is really Daniel from the Bible, he just took Elton John's form. He speaks several languages from the Middle East, but also English. The real Elton John is still happily living on the Earth. Ernest, Daniel can help you. He is my dear friend, he is part of me, but that would be another and long story. He can connect you with culinary experts and if you want also with some of the famous movie and cinema stars from America and elsewhere who have died. I think you would love it. He is the biggest expert I know regarding dreams. I would suggest you ask him how you can send more lovely dreams to Sylvia. I'll leave you with him now, I have to go."

I heard the call for return in my headphones from the Earth. I have no idea how their conversation proceeded and what Ernest did afterward.

I was obviously curious how it went and only two days later visited with Daniel. He told me:

"I asked your friend if he would like to go to the Culinary

Institute There or maybe to Hollywood There. I explained to him that in Hollywood There the inhabitants are planning new movies and influencing movie makers on the Earth to execute their ideas. Unlike on the Earth, all the departed stars are very accessible, friendly and they discuss everything together. He was excited and asked me to take him there immediately.

"Did you tell him, Daniel, that Hollywood There is not in the Park in Focus 27, but in the Belief System Territories and Focus 26?"

"I did not have a chance. He saw John Wayne and Tony Curtis waiting for him, waving for him to come, so he hurried through their gate. He is still Earth bound and you should just let him to enjoy his newfound freedoms and joys."

Chapter 41
PLAUTUS

"No man is wise enough by himself." (Titus Maccius Plautus)

In the previous four chapters I returned to the issues of the departed souls living in the Earth Life System. I also described how I was spiritually helping some people still physically living in their physical bodies on the Earth. I am aware that many people among us prefer to deal with and talk about issues regarding only their physical lives. Talking about the afterlife is a strange and weird proposition for them. That is absolutely O.K. by me. I just wonder why they do not want to know whether there is a hereafter and what can happen to them if it does exist.

Some people can be a little more willing to talk about another possibility for the physical life, hoping that they could do better the next time. The topic of reincarnation is certainly a favorite subject for a variety of New Age movements. But the analysis of reincarnation's ways and options is often limited by looking primarily for physical signs and proofs by a strictly materialistic methodology. For example, seeing somebody with a scar or other body irregularity is understood as a trace from an injury or death by a weapon in a past life. Experiences like kids talking about their past lives are often seen as obvious proof that reincarnation does happen indeed.

However, the core of my metaphysical research and travels was always, is, and will be in a more important area. I am much more interested in messages, advice, and teachings from those on the other side. Focusing on how my guides and star friends look does not make any sense to me. Often, I do not even have time and space for that. I am busy with the receiving, collecting, and unwinding of the ROTEs they are giving me, as described in many places in my books. Pondering, for example, about a Reptilian having or not having a tail is a rather bizarre issue for me. Instead, I want to know why a Reptilian showed up, what she or he wants, or what messages there are for me. Often, even well-known New Age personalities can emphasize truly insignificant details rather than the core and essence of an experience. Not to have access to information from the metaphysical world is understandable, but I really have a problem with shallow thinking.

As I have documented many times in my books, the higher you raise your vibrations in your metaphysical travels toward the Ultimate Source, the less important the sensory perceptions and the form of the vehicle for your communication is. But, on the other hand, lowering the vibrations means that the sensory perceptions and vehicle forms are more and more important. Many people believe that only what can be perceived by the five senses truly exists. My disregard of this idea gave me tremendous freedom in my travels and gave me my wings.

Despite all of what I just described, I have occasionally looked for connections between my current physical life and the past lives I have uncovered. I paid special attention to two of my past lives which were the most important in my spiritual development on this planet. I described them in *How to Kiss the Universe*. In my intentionally planned trip to Switzerland, I looked for the place where I lived as Menev and was meeting my main spiritual teacher, Michael the Gardener, in the 15th century. And I found it. On the same trip, I also learned unintentionally about coming as an old Viking shaman to France in the 9th century. I also mentioned in my first book that I had concluded that I would not need to travel to Rome to look for connections regarding my third most important reincarnation as the Roman playwright Plautus since his life was well documented.

However, in early February 2021, I read an article about the historical origins of the word religion in our local newspaper Birmingham News. The article was from a young assistant professor of Religious Studies, Samuel L. Boyd, at the University of Colorado in Boulder. According to him, the plays by Plautus were one of the first works to use the Latin word *religio*. As Boyd described it, *religio* originally meant something like restraints or scruples. And, I would add the word, divisions, to the meaning. I am always emphasizing that I have nothing against religions. As I described in *How to Kiss the Universe* in several chapters explaining the Belief System Territories, a variety of religions on our planet are giving people at least some direction and temporary help in their search for meaning. But on the other hand, they are dividing people and putting them into boxes. This obvious connection in my thinking to Plautus inspired me to see if I could find more information. I did find several other connections. I am including them here as a short illustration about what is more important for me than any physical features.

Plautus used a lot of proverbs in his works. When I try to explain something, I like to use them too, sometimes even obsessively looking for a suitable one. I have a proverb for almost any situation. His jokes were full of jest, and I have that tendency, too. Sometimes I wish my remarks and jokes could be softer and less spicy. Plautus considered the relationship of the father and son to be important; I think like that as well. My Dad taught me to love geography and history and inspired me to be creative, to always look around and be interested in my surroundings. I loved him very much, even though I wished he would drink less. And I dearly love my sons, Viktor, and Boris.

The name Plautus can mean flat footed, and I am that also. I had to take care of my plantar fasciitis a few years back. I was always fascinated by the great Carthaginian general Hannibal who threatened Rome during the Second Punic War in the years 218 to 201 A.D. Plautus was 36 years old when the war started. Soon Hannibal was all over Italia and threatened Rome itself. Plautus was 53 years old when Hannibal and Carthage were finally defeated. He was born north of Rome in the region of Umbria and became a naturalized citizen of Rome. I am a naturalized citizen of the United States.

These are just little connections of my current self to one of my several Roman incarnations. They explain why I have had a drive to write, inspire people throughout my whole life, and help them to recognize what is important. I also wish for them to live life in a simple way with a light heart and be funny. But, dear eventual Debunker, if you would ask me how I looked at that time, what I liked to wear and eat, who my friends were, or anything about my plays, I cannot tell you. It is simply not important to me. Once I tried to see if I would be able to get some flashback and went to see Plautus' play "Merchant" (Mercator in Latin) played by students at the George Mason University in Northern Virginia. But I did not have any flashbacks. Maybe you can figure out how to get them from your past lives and then you can let me know. I will gladly take and try your advice.

Chapter 42
ASCENSION TEST

"Ascension is the triumph of mastered emotions; a process of gaining clarity in the darkness of blind spots and struggles, allowing you to perceive with the karmic intelligence of the Soul." (Ka Chinery)

At this point of my writings, I must return to August of 2018, because I want to emphasize something utterly important for anyone who is contemplating ascension into the highest realms of spiritual reality.

After long and arduous work, I finished designing the cover and was ready to publish *How to Kiss the Universe*. I felt exceptionally good about it and was ready to go to my real home, my true home, the true heaven. I knew it was not time for that yet, and that it will come only after I finally leave my shell, my box, my vehicle, my physical body. But I decided to try to get close to it even for a moment. I went to sleep with such a wish.

While dreaming, I decided to vibrationally rise as high as I could. When I reached Focus 120, I knew I was right under the Ultimate Membrane. It was so overwhelming that I was afraid of not coming back into my body and started to scream. Juanzetta woke me up and I realized that I really did not want to leave for good yet.

I had difficulty to go back to sleep and had to get out of bed even though it was right in the middle of the night. It was so powerful! I realized that I had executed a direct ascension to God and saw The Source of Everything vibrationally right above me. I even speculated that I could be in Christ's direct bloodline, but I did not have any spiritual message or proof of something like that. This thought happened because of my disciplined consistent and steady approach to spiritual and metaphysical progress.

I will remember that marvelous night for the rest of my physical life. I suddenly knew I would not need a teacher, a guru, or anybody like that anymore. I became complete. I realized again in a different and direct way that I had become a Chunk of the Infinite Sea of Bonded I-There Clusters, ready to disappear into the infinity of the *Source* and become one with God. I knew that this experience was a direct gift from the Ultimate Creator.

This happened in Washington D.C., and what was amazing was that I had left my Hemi-Sync in Birmingham and had such an experience without its support. And Juanzetta told me in the morning that she had not awakened me at all. Obviously, I continued my contemplation and speculation about being vibrationally so far away from my physical body.

Chapter 43
BABY, KEYS AND LADIES

"Some women choose to follow men; some choose to follow their dreams." *(Lady Gaga)*

I wanted to practice working with Daniel and dreams some more. I usually have three intentions for my meditations, so I decided to put the following three dreams into my next inquiry. Here they are:

Juanzetta and I have a movie night every Friday and on one of those we decided to see *Starman,* starring Jeff Bridges. Afterwards, I had a dream about being pregnant and expecting a baby very soon. I asked the male nurse who came to help me whether I would have bowel movements. He answered that I would, a lot, and told me I better go immediately.

In the second one, I was dreaming about retiring from the Voice of America. I was wandering around inside the building reluctant to return my keys, speculating that maybe I could keep them.

My third dream was about being at a public ceremony or competition. We were all sitting in the waiting room. Michelle Obama, Hillary Clinton, and Oprah Winfrey were also there complaining about the need to wait. Juanzetta rented a car and we drove away for a break in the waiting. What is amazing is that Juanzetta had a remarkably interesting and similar dream the same night about being with me at a party, and we had to leave together. The longer we are together, shared experiences like that are becoming more common.

I again used the Lifeline take home exercise for my inquiry. When I got to my Special Place, Daniel was there waiting, and he again looked like a young Elton John.
"Why do you look like that again?" I asked him.
"I think it is appropriate. It helped you find me. I was afraid that it would never happen. I have a lot to tell you, to help

you and advise you, Jozef."

"What, are you an Elohim too?" I was curious.

"I am not, but I want to be an Elohim, I want to go home with you. You said you were going to take me with you, remember? I am part of you, after all. Jozef, you are understanding your dreams better than other people, but you can still learn more, just like when you were with me 2500 years ago."

"Well then, let us start Daniel. Why was I dreaming about having a baby? It is about my second book, isn't it? Is my second book my baby, and am I going to have a difficult birth?"

"That is right, and not only that. You must be careful not to release a lot of shit with it. You understood that too, didn't you?"

"Yes, I did, I kind of knew what that meant."

"That is why you had to go to the bathroom before the birth of the baby, to get that out of you. Michael told me to help you more now, especially with dreams."

"Thanks, Daniel. What about trying to return those keys? Do I have to do that?"

"No, Jozef, you just do not have to only return them, you should keep them. Those keys are replicable. They also represent your books. When someone finds either book or buys it, they will get a key to their soul. They might be able to completely unlock their inner and outer self, like you did. When they keep the key, which they have acquired, another one is automatically replicated and is ready to be used by someone else."

"Splendid, Daniel. How about those three ladies at the event, Michelle Obama, Hillary Clinton, and Oprah Winfrey? What does that mean? I like their personalities and charismas and sometimes dream about them; they are liberals like my Juanzetta. However, I have never dreamt about all three of them at the same time."

"Well, Jozef, they are three very influential women in your country, are they not? I sent you their images through the dream, Jozef. Women, women, women! You must find a way to involve more women into accepting and even promoting your books. You understand that women need to have more influential powers to change the world for better. Look at Nature which you like so much. Who in the animal kingdom is securing and guiding their kind toward surviving more, male or female?"

I had to admit that it was the females.

"You did a little mistake with *How to Kiss the Universe*. It is a book more for a man than a woman, and females recognized that. Unless you could be on the same stage with someone well known, like one of those three ladies, for example, your book will not become a bestseller."

Now I had to counteract and explain something to Daniel:

"I do not really care about that, Daniel. You know, sometimes I feel like Forest Gump when he stopped his long run. His few followers in the movie stopped, too, and one of them said:

"Wait, he wants to say something!"

And Forest calmly announced in his southern accent:

"Ah'm tired, I just want to go home!"

"I feel like that too, Daniel."

Daniel nodded his Elton John head and it seemed to me that he had understood what I had said when we parted.

Chapter 44
NEW BROTHER

"Blessed are the pure in heart: for they shall see God."
(Matthew 5:8)

After I developed my good relationship with Daniel, I started to have a variety of interesting and sometimes weird dreams. However, I knew they were always representing something I needed to think about. The dreams were also very entertaining, and I had a lot of fun. There was no doubt that Daniel was enjoying our newfound connection as well.

Juanzetta and I were also busy with our permanently moving from Washington D.C. in the second half of June 2020. My expectation of leaving my body permanently before my 72nd birthday had not materialized. We decided to spend the sunsets of our lives together. Her beautiful condo in Redmont Park in Birmingham became the obvious natural choice for that.

We settled into this majestic place enjoying peaceful days and quiet nights. However, in the middle of July I was awakened by what I thought was a power hammer driving poles into the ground. That sound used to wake us up often in the morning in Washington D.C. when they started to raise another apartment building on our grounds there. Juanzetta, however, told me that she did not hear anything.

After a series of unsuccessful meditations in the Earth Life System using the Lifeline take home exercise in previous weeks, I decided that evening just to go without any intention into a much higher vibrational space. I did not expect anything to happen. I apparently clicked out and was having a pleasant nap while enjoying myself on the other side. I was awakened in the middle of the Starlines II CD by a strong pilot signal. I was sure that such a signal was not a part of the recording because I had used it many times before. I was in the upper forty focus levels where the CD takes you. I saw a large pyramid with the Sun next to it on one side and Ra standing on the other side holding his golden cane like instrument.

"You, Lord Ra? I did not expect to meet you, what happened?" I asked, obviously surprised by his presence.

"I think that you need a little bit of Cane-fu!" *Ra* answered.

"What do you mean by that, Lord Ra?"

"Do not call me that Jozef, you are my Brother so call me Brother! You are now one of us, you are going to be in our Highest Order. We taught you a lot and you just put the money into your pocket and disappeared when you were supposed to organize the show?' I came to lift up your Kokoro now!"

"Oh, Brother, did you send me all those weird dreams?"

Now I remembered the dream from the morning. I was in the attic in a run-down house with a group of people who were preparing a paranormal show. Someone gave me a bunch of bills and I stuck them in my pocket. One lady was trying to do introductions and form the working ensemble. I did not like it, nodded my head at another guy and we ran away. They immediately chased us. I was not sure if I would be able to find my car and heard someone scream:

"It's him, get him!" And I woke up.

"Yes, I did send you the dream. I am here to do some necessary dirty work. Someone must do it. You did not run far in the dream, did you? You could not even find your car which is your physical body!"

"I am sorry, my Brother, what is this all about?"

Ra, however, was determined to teach me something. He said he woke me up in the morning by the sound of pounding with a jack hammer, using my memory of that from Washington D.C.

"There is a lot of shit around you, Jozef, isn't there?" Ra shocked me with his straightforward and spicy talk and wanted to continue, but I interrupted him:

"Are we going to talk about my other weird dream, did you send that one too?" And Ra nodded his head. He meant my third dream that morning.

Dear Reader, please forgive me here also for my straightforward and spicy approach. If you read *How to Kiss the Universe*, you know that I am normally not holding (metaphorically) a napkin in front of my mouth when speaking, unless we are protecting ourselves from the coronavirus. I am genuinely reporting what happened. And if you think that stories like this reflect some part of my personality, just think about it carefully. Think about straightforwardness and hypocrisy.

I was dreaming of being on a high ladder in the hallway somewhere and defecating. The brown turd fell on the ground and created an almost perfect circle. Someone stepped on the edge of it, even though I tried to warn him. I stepped down, wrapped some of it in a sheet and tossed it into the garbage can nearby. When I wanted to clean the rest, it was already gone without any trace. Ra continued in his lecture:

"You ran up the ladder with your own shit and then you just dropped it down. At least, you realized that you must clean after yourself, but we were the ones who made it disappear completely. You tried the easy way, Brother!"

"And you, Brother Ra, will you finally tell me what's up?"

"You have to fight to deliver your messages both to those who are willing and want to hear it and to those who don't want to hear it. Do not give up, do not resign. Revive your efforts in spreading your knowledge around, Brother!"

"You really want me to do it in such an environment, Ra? Our country is being torn apart, many people have gotten crazy, and they hate each other. I never thought something like what is happening now could happen, especially not in the United States of America. I have believed in her with my whole heart!"

"It is going to get worse, Jozef Daniel. There are and there will be every day more and more fakes and frauds around. Your country is not genuine anymore. People are losing integrity, fear will be steadily rising, and violence and killings will spread even more. Only a few brave ones are willing to step in and reverse it. Your country will stop functioning and will rise again only after a spiritual metaphysical revival. And you should be part of that process. Do not just impatiently run back home to the Source. Do it after you shed your physical body if you want to, but while you have your physical vehicle, fight for your mission. Fight for your Juanzetta, your kids, your friends, friends of friends, family and strangers, for everybody on the planet."

I was thinking about asking Ra to do something personal for me, but at the end of the encounter I decided not to. I was thinking about his criticizing my attitude, about what we were discussing and about my options. I realized that humankind is full of hypocrisy. People are pretending to be who they are not. They are forgetting about their own lives by comparing themselves to others. They want to live lives driven not by their own wishes and desires but based on what others tell them.

Staring at screens has become a new religion. The Internet brought tremendous information for anyone who has a smartphone, but also, as my Juanzetta once said, the Internet became the equalizer. Individual responsibility and judgements are quickly disappearing. In their place, unjustified constant complaining, finger pointing and blaming others has become the new social norms. The span of human attention is becoming shorter and shorter, many people organize their lives based on shots, headlines, and soundbites.

I realized with relief that I had no metaphysical duty to be obedient. I rose, as Ra told me, to be equal among equals. I do not have to do anything anymore. I am a free, unlimited, timeless, and completely independent spiritual and metaphysical being! As such, I shall enjoy my free will and the lightness of being on this planet and beyond after I shed my physical body.

I was thinking to suggest to Ra that he should rather do such a job himself by incarnating into a human body on the Earth. He or she (if he would incarnate into a female body) could go to school himself, grow up, find The Monroe Institute, then spend a lot of money there and write the story about his experiences. That it is what I would like to tell him, but I will not. I am sure that he could do a better job than I did. However, that does not mean that I will not continue in my own efforts to get the message out.

Chapter 45
POSSIBLE FUTURE

"After this I looked, and there before me was a door standing open in heaven. And the voice I had first heard speaking to me like a trumpet said: "Come up here, and I will show you what must take place after this." (Revelation 4:1)

Throughout all my life I have had apocalyptic dreams. I am often dreaming about floods, wars, earthquakes, and planetary destruction. I will mention here some of my dreams as I remember them from before I developed the habit of recording everything upon awakening.

In one such dream, I came to an interplanetary conference on a large plateau where a speaker's dais was prepared for someone to deliver a speech. I was in the crowd and all around me were other people and intelligent beings waiting for the speaker. The speaker came and it was God. God said:

"Now the time has come to end our experiment with two legged men. They shall be finished," and I woke up.

In another undated dream, there was a huge cosmic ship hovering over our heads. We had been notified that our Earth would be destroyed with deadly rays the next day. The God who had created us said that the rays would penetrate the whole planet. All I could think to do was clean my fish tank, wanting my fish to live the last day of their lives in a nice clean environment. When I finished cleaning, I decided to gather my family. I had started to call my wife and kids when I woke up.

In October 2007, I was dreaming about being in Bratislava. Very dense black clouds were hovering above the city, and they started to fall and crash and destroy the buildings. Everybody was in a panic. I ran under the Archway of Michael. Nobody knew what to do. Suddenly one man sat down and started to scream:

"We all forgot to pray, we all forgot to pray! Let us pray

now, let's everybody pray now!"

As we prayed, the sky started to be clearer and clearer, and the clouds were disappearing. I learned about the meaning of this dream only four and a half years later in a meditation in March 2012. The man who had asked the people to pray in the dream was Robert Monroe. But his prayer was meant to inspire the people on Earth to look for Love and real meaning and the purpose of life inside their minds, not outside in the opinions of other people. It was also a challenge for me to follow up on his discoveries and inspirations, and to make my continuation of his work public so that anyone could start to make changes within himself or herself as needed.

In April 2011, I had a dream after just about two hours of sleeping. Water was rising very quickly in the streets of the town, and I saw people running in shock and panic. I was also looking for some higher ground when I saw a house with a ladder going up into its attic. When I climbed up thinking they would follow me, the people below me started to accuse me of stealing their ladder instead. They were trying to climb onto the house in every way possible. A voice from a loudspeaker was asking people to stay calm and wait. But instead, they were screaming:

"They are coming, they are coming," and the panic intensified.

Apparently, some entities were coming after the people, and they were very afraid. When I woke up, I had the disturbing feeling that I had just possibly seen the future. I called on Hadien and asked him:

"What was my dream about? Did I see the future? Why were people accusing me of stealing the ladder, but at the same time trying to climb up on the building?"

"Yes indeed, you saw a possible future on the Earth. There shall be many floods before the Great Destruction. The people tried to follow you after seeing your cool behavior, believing that you held the secret of how to help them and save them. They did not understand that you would be able to help them only spiritually after they expired, but not physically while they were still alive," answered Hadien.

"Who were those looking for me and chasing me?"

"Those were the secret government killing squads. In that situation, they were mercifully killing everyone they could find because there would be no food or shelter available. They justified their work as the need to lessen suffering and to prepare the planet and any surviving individuals for a new beginning."

I kept thinking a lot about that dream, especially speculating what governments really could do for people in such situations. I decided to call on Hadien again and ask. But when I reached Focus 42, instead of him, Ra approached me. When I posed my question about it to Ra, he immediately suggested a trip where he could show me how governments can misguide people into false beliefs and thereby manipulate them. He told me he knew about my worries immediately when I showed up in Focus 42, because he could read my mind whenever I was there. He again emphasized that I had to learn about both sides of spiritual reality and the manifested universe, not only about the good, but also about the existing trickery and deceiving. He took me to Andromeda again, talking during our trip:

"First, I want to tell you that I am not a spiritual robot. But it is okay for you to have suspicions like that because they make you stronger and more aware. I will show you a planet where they control and manipulate the population with holographic images. Do not worry about where the planet is, you would not be able to locate her anyway. But if you need a name, let us call her Goldilocks. And you people from Earth would never be able to get to her in your antique physical spaceships. Traveling in the physical environment is awfully slow. The fastest possible speed is the speed of light. Some physical civilizations have reached that speed, but as you know, with your technology it would take many generations for you to travel here. And, as you are doing now, you can make it here with only part of your consciousness, but not with your physical body from Earth."

Ra's intergalactic ship stopped, hovering just above the planet. I could see cigar shaped ships hovering below us all around the planet. I suddenly saw a light beam going down from one of the ships to the surface, creating a huge explosion followed by fire. Ra continued in his explanations: "All the ships you see, Menev, are holographic creations. The global government of Goldilocks has claimed that it has created a protective shield so that the alien cigar ships cannot land. According to the government, aliens can sometimes land and attack and destroy towns on the planet. Sometimes it looks like the government of the planet destroys some of the alien ships. They have, however, created a holographic state of permanent siege and war. That has enabled the government, claiming to protect the people of the planet, to tax them into the slavery conditions. Some greedy globalists on the Earth are trying to do the same as you see here."

"What can we, what can I do about that?" I asked terrified.

"You can talk about your experience, about what you saw here, but they will laugh at you," answered Ra.

"Can you intervene at our planet?" I pleaded.

"We do not intervene when civilizations reach your level. We were intervening on your Earth in ancient times when you needed help to move on. When societies are primitive, there are more interventions from the spiritual plane. When societies advance, we intervene less and less until the interventions stop entirely. You on the Earth are already at that stage."

Ra took me back home. I could not get out of my mind the unpleasant feeling that the same thing could happen to us as had happened on Goldilocks. I just wish that we would be smarter than the folks on that distant world in Andromeda.

Much later, when I had almost finished this book, I had another dream of this kind. It was in the August 2020, coronavirus times, with protests and violence on the streets of our cities and the historical November 2020 presidential elections on the horizon. I saw a large bomb coming down on the town, but it did not explode. It hit the ground and stuck in an upright position. The bomb was almost as big as the skyscrapers around it. I thought we should get ready to leave the city with my car but realized that I really had no idea where to go. Juanzetta and I looked out of the window and saw terrified children screaming and running from the nearby school.

Then, I was on the street and a young black man ran into me; he was also terrified. I tried to comfort him and calm him down, but he continued running and I woke up. I visited Daniel in my Special Place in the Park and asked him for an explanation. He said:

"The bomb represents the division of your society in the country now. It is so big because it portrays the possibility of tremendous destruction. The buildings can be destroyed, whole cities and towns can be devastated. It can blow up at any time, or never. I cannot tell you when, Jozef, because I do not know. Saying the exact time when it would blow up does not reflect the way the system on your planet was set up by the Creators. You can get glimpses of the future, but the future is not guaranteed because everything is happening at the same time. The physical environment of C1 would not have a true purpose and there would be no sense in its existence if you could exactly predict future events in your local space and time. That is how the Creators designed your physical environment. Prophecies will always be foggy and uncertain because the future is not written in stone. The future always has alternatives and possibilities, but you understand that because you understand the bubbling."

"How about the looking for the car, is that about my physical body?" I asked.

"Not only the physical body but also all the spiritual vehicles you are using. You know how to use them like you do your physical car, you just do not know when the time will come to leave."

Then he continued:

"Children would suffer the most if the bomb would blow,

that is why they were terrified in the dream. The young black men represented by the guy you met would be at the mercy of chaos and violence, which can accelerate beyond any control."

I once asked why I have apocalyptic dreams and sometimes even devilish dreams and thoughts all the time, as if someone would be trying to incite me to do something bad or harmful to other people. Early on in my spiritual journey I was afraid that such entities really could harm me and destroy me. I asked about that and learned:

"You shall continue to have those; they are part of your human nature and your mission on the planet. However, because of your spiritual training, they can only harm you as much as if someone would hit you with a silk scarf. You are strong and you reject them automatically and they quickly learn your power."

Chapter 46
STAGED INVASION

"If aliens visited us, the outcome would be much as when Columbus landed in America, which didn't turn out well for the Native Americans." (Stephen Hawking)

Throughout my life, I have been receiving a variety of warnings about our planet, what could happen to her and what could happen to the humans living on Earth. Possible threats to our life on earth are very well known, such as pandemics, asteroid hits, cataclysmic earthquakes, eruptions of super-volcanos, sun flares and giant cosmic explosions.

Then, there are also our man-made threats like a nuclear war, catastrophic pollutions, climate changes and a destruction of our environment. But there is also the threat of an alien invasion. It might be a physical invasion, or malevolent beings could possibly try to destroy us by infiltrating into our minds and eventually also by taking over our bodies. But I believe in the power of the human spirit, our love of human life and our determination to find the way not only to resist but to overcome such catastrophes. I had a dream in April 2012 in which we did exactly that.

We were told by our leaders and the media that we were being attacked by a huge force of fire and power waves coming from space unexpectedly in the direction of our planet. We should all prepare to die. I was in a radio and television transmitter on the hill with both of my sons. Surprisingly, people were calm even though they were horrified. Everybody seemed to be doing their regular business. A person who was in charge in the tower gave me something like a big chunk of meat and told me to take it down by the elevator.

It was only couple of minutes before the end of our lives were supposed to happen. I was wondering what sense it made to go down, but I complied. The elevator was not working, so I started to walk down the stairs and felt the heat coming from outside. Everything around me was shaking.

I experienced a sudden shift in my dream and found myself on the beach not far from the tower. I was with Juanzetta and other people. We were expecting a tsunami wave and were ready to die. It did not happen even though we saw huge waves coming from a distance. Suddenly everything became quiet. We looked at the tower and people were calmly walking down and out. I asked a young woman what happened. She said that our scientists had figured out the way to defeat the aliens. They had analyzed their structure and disabled the aliens' nervous systems.

I went back to the tower and saw a schematic vertical drawing of an alien's structure on the wall downstairs. A round head was on the top and next to it a question mark. The head was connected through the neck to a square which symbolized the upper body; it had two apparent limbs. Then, there was a triangle leading to a star in the middle of the structure with a remark next to it saying that it was their nervous center. Then, there was another square to symbolize the lower part of body with two limbs, and then another unnamed triangle. At the bottom, there was another little circle like a lower head.

The people who were gathered around the drawing explained to me that our scientists were able to identify the alien's nervous center. When they hit the aliens in their nervous centers, they blew apart and then dissolved. But the scientists were unable to understand the aliens' intelligence centers or identify their motivation for attacking us. That is why they had placed a question mark next to the upper head.

I walked upstairs in the tower. My younger son Boris was still there. He was excited and described how he saw one of the aliens being blown up. He said that the military, along with our scientists, had let the aliens come as close to us as possible for the most effective counterattack. I asked Boris where my older son Viktor was, and he said that he had already gone back to work. When I woke up, I naturally wanted to know more about my dream.

When I reached Alpha Squared, my friend Hadien was already on the platform, and he was pacing like he was waiting for someone! It was very funny to see hundreds of his tiny legs moving for the first time. His pyramidal body was sliding along as if he were sitting on the back of a caterpillar. I had to laugh, but he was serious:
"I have to warn you, Menev, that you should not misunderstand your dream. You should know that something like an alien attack can be completely fake and staged. The governments on many planets are creating a simulated invasion by using holographic and other techniques."
"Why would they do that, to scare us or what?"
I could not believe in this kind of conspiracy on our planet, even though I remembered very well my trip to Goldilocks with Ra where I saw something terribly similar.
"No, they would just like to show the alleged capabilities of the governing elites."
"Did I have precognition; did I see the future, Hadien? And if I did, are you saying that aliens did not attack us at all?"
"A possible future, my friend. But it does not have to happen like that at all. The future always has possibilities. It is up to you people whether it happens or not. Look how smart the stagers of the attack were. They said they could not analyze the aliens' brains and their intentions. They will insist that they could not communicate with aliens. And there are no traces of the alien bodies left. The government would say the aliens were destroyed before reaching your space, even though they got so close. You should always do some second guessing if you hear about invasion threats. Right now, we have the malevolent spiritual creatures around your planet pretty much in check. I just wanted you to know that."

Chapter 47
FREE WILL AND SUICIDE

"Man, what are you talking about? Me in chains? You may fetter my leg but my will, not even Zeus himself can overpower." (Epictetus, The Discourses)

From September 2008 through October 2011, I participated in 13 programs at The Monroe Institute. I covered most of happenings about that period of my spiritual journey in *How to Kiss the Universe*. However, while going through my diaries again, I found something interesting in October 2011. I want to share it. While using the Lifeline take home CD, I had the intention to learn about free will and suicide. Here is what I received:

"Even though you are an unlimited spiritual being, your free will is limited by your development. You can do anything you wish, but you cannot process information which you would not understand, even if your free will is enabling you to try to do that. You have to use your free will wisely and in line with the current stage of your development."

"How about suicide?" I asked.

"Talking about suicide can be like talking about leaving school because it was too hard to study. We are talking about suicide which is not justified."

"When is suicide justified?" I asked.

"As we said, you can do whatever you wish because of your free will. If you want to talk about justification, we can say that it could be in the case of unbearable physical pain. But psychological and mental problems can be connected to your inability to study in the school you entered voluntarily with your own free will. Your free will enables you to quit anytime you want. However, when you do that, you would have to deal with consequences on the other side. There is no punishment in any form here. However, quitting school means the slowing down of your development in most cases."

Much later in my spiritual journey, late in 2016, I was looking for the daughter of a dear friend who had suddenly departed. Juanzetta and I had a suspicion that it could have been suicide, or even foul play. Juanzetta asked me to see if I could find her in Focus 23 in the astral plane. I had not done any rescues or retrievals of the departed for a while at that time. I could not find her anywhere and went to the Park. My guides asked me where I had been for so long. I wondered how they knew it was so long when time does not exist there. They said they were aware of the flow of earthly local time, even if they were not using it. They tried to help me find her, but they could not do it either.

According to their explanations, the frequencies of freshly departed souls from Earth fluctuate in the first few days. They go suddenly sharply up and down especially when the death-departure has not been expected, like in the case of an accident, foul play or even suicide. Souls expecting or knowing they are dying can settle quickly and effectively on a chosen frequency and, thus, can be located easier. Their frequencies are more stable even shortly after a departure and it makes them easier to find.

Chapter 48
BUTTERFLIES

"When her big, gorgeous monarch butterfly changed to a cloud of small butterflies, she spread the message of the wonderful butterfly type of Love at the end of the human life all around her and everywhere." (How to Kiss the Universe, Chapter 80)

When I thought that this book would be finished by the conversation with Ra, I received yet another interesting and inviting dream. In that dream I was driving on a wide highway and the traffic was very dense and slow. It looked like no car would get anywhere soon. I decided to try to find a shortcut but had to go against the traffic for twenty or thirty yards in the opposite direction to cross the highway through the dividing median to reach the country road I saw.

I was driving comfortably on that country road for a while when suddenly a high wire fence appeared in front of me. Through it, I could see incredibly beautiful green grass shining in the rays of the sun. The meadow did not seem to have any boundaries. After a while, I manifested a gate in the fence, and it appeared. I drove into the field and received the question of whether I would like to stay there. I was not sure about it and started preparing to go back. But before I could do that, I woke up.

Just out of curiosity I went into a high vibrational meditation the same evening. I wanted to see who would show up. I wanted to ask them why I did not die yet and what could be ahead for me in the future in my physical life. When I reached the high vibrational space of the upper forty focus levels, a foggy silhouette was approaching. When the image cleared, I recognized Ruala, my female star friend. She had on her favorite white and red alternating colors dress with the flickering giant heart in the upper part of her body.

"You, My Lady? I am surprised to see you now. Did you send me my dream this morning? What is the message in it?"

"You brought a lot of questions with you, didn't you Jozef? You wanted to know why you did not die before your 72nd birthday as you had expected. It did not happen for a reason. Did you really want to leave your Juanzetta alone? It is not the time for either of you to leave yet."

"I would not mind, My Lady, I really wouldn't mind going. My physical body is getting tired, even if my soul is full of life more than ever before."

"Do not call me My Lady, Jozef. I am your Sister. I also represent all the female lovers and friends you have met in your earthly life. And, I am also your final giant butterfly, your Juanzetta. You also asked about your future. That was in the dream I sent you. You stepped out of the physical materialistic crowd; you even had to drive a long way against the crowd. Then you found your private road leading you to the meadow without boundaries. Look now at you and Juanzetta, you are like beautiful butterflies for the rest of your physical lives. Love each other until you die, and live together in peace, mutual respect, harmony and compassion."

Ruala created a new scene for me. I again saw unbelievably beautiful shiny green flickering grass. I could see two monarch butterflies flying in a loving dance. Then suddenly, zillions of other butterflies of all colors imaginable joined the dance. The sun rays were luminating the magical scene.

"Jozef, you and Juanzetta, you are not alone. You are One with all the other spiritual beings who have reached the same maturity as you have in the All That Exists. And like you, they are ready to go to their True Homes at any time."

Chapter 49
FIANCÉ

"Promises are only as strong as the person who gives them."
(Stephen Richards)

The spiritual journey can be very romantic if you are lucky enough to have a partner, wife, or husband whose opinions about the metaphysical world and spirituality are close to those of yours. I am incredibly lucky that Juanzetta and I found each other. While I was going through my diaries again in the process of writing this book, I found some additional fragments I want to share with you.

I had a beautiful dream in October 2011 when our romantic loving relationship had started to go at full steam. We were climbing up in an extremely high tower by a very narrow staircase. When we reached the top, it opened out into a big round bowl. A beautiful set of electric swings were ready for us there and we took an exciting ride around. You probably could, Dear Reader, also explain what that dream meant. If you raise your vibrations enough, you can get to a wonderful place. Dreaming about an elevator, climbing stairs, or even flying almost always means just that.

The manifestation of our wishes really can happen if we are sincere and determined about them. On New Year's 2012, Juanzetta told me about her manifestation of me. She has a custom of writing down her New Year expectations. On New Year's Day of 2010, after several years of being single, she decided that it was going to be the year when she would like to meet her new guy.

She wrote down his expected attributes: he should be sixty to seventy years old, at least six feet tall, in good health, taking good care of his body, have a nice body, be fiscally sound, like to travel, like to cook, enjoy eating good food and have a good sense of humor. He did not have to live in Birmingham but should be willing to come there often for a visit, and he should be able to have sex and enjoy it. It would not bother her if he were from a foreign country, because she wanted foreign words to be whispered into her ear. On the last day of the Starlines program in July 2010 where we had met, I hugged her under the stars and whispered in her ear: "Máš krásne oči (You have beautiful eyes)."

After getting to know me better, she finally told me that all her manifestations had come true. She also remarked that she had received a bonus, because I was also romantic even though she had not asked for that.

Later I was dreaming about being with Juanzetta and some of her friends. A lady friend of hers said:

"Juanzetta, you look much younger than your age and you are shining." Juanzetta answered:

"Of course, I am very happy, because I have a fiancé."

When inquiring about this with my guides, I received the following explanation:

"Having a fiancé or fiancée means promise. It is a mutual promise to help each another after you finally leave the physical life on Earth. One of you, either you or Juanzetta, will depart earlier and shall be waiting to help the other in the initial stages of transition. Even though both of you are strongly bound for the Park, there is still a little danger, especially when passing through the ring of Focus 23 and the Belief System Territories. You can be misdirected by someone who has not liked your activities on Earth.

Having a fiancé or fiancée is a promise to prevent that and help each other secure a safe passage to the Park. It is not only a promise, but also a security. Not many people on Earth can build such strong ties to another spiritual being of the same quality. When you eventually die, besides everything else you already know about the other side and the transition, simply look for your fiancé or fiancée and ask for his or her help."

I must add here that Juanzetta is now wearing a small, tiny spiritual fiancée ring that I gave her for Christmas after receiving that message. That ring was joined by two guard rings when we married in 2016.

Chapter 50
MULTIPLE PARTNERS

"Wherever there is a human being, there is an opportunity for kindness." (Seneca)

Many of us throughout a lifetime on this planet have had several partners with whom we have fallen in love. We men can even sometimes be in love with two or more women at the same time. Sometimes, this can also happen to a woman. Thus, you may ask how it is going to be on the other side in the spiritual realm after we die here. How will we deal with the multiple partners we had in this life? I was asking this question myself from time to time, so finally I decided to ask it in an altered state while in the spiritual realm.

I was pondering early on in my spiritual journey that it would be wonderful to have a spiritual partner in the metaphysical world who would be a combination of the best two or even more incarnated human beings on our planet during my physical life. As a man, I thought it would be great to have a partner composed of the best part of the ladies with whom I had gotten involved. So, I asked about it and here is what I have learned:

"Merging your beloved spiritual beings is not possible. They are unique. There is however no jealousy here, here everything is One. You are multi-dimensional, and you can be in many places in many times with many beings. If you would need to separate your feelings for whatever reason, you can do it through your Higher-Higher Self."

I fully understood that after I had an interesting dream in November 2011. In the dream, I was in bed with Elena, my first wife, and we were passionately kissing each other. It was very real indeed. I was thinking in the dream that I would have to confess it to Juanzetta. While I was pushing my hand up Elena's thigh, I woke up. When I inquired about it, my guides told me that Elena entered my dream to tell me that she approved of my relationship with Juanzetta, and that she was happy that I had found her. When I was sharing my dream with Juanzetta, I was surprised to learn that she had had a similar dream on the same day about her deceased husband Charlie. When they were about to start making love, she woke up.

A week later I asked about it in a meeting with Gardener:

"How do we deal with the issue of having had different love partners on the Earth when we leave the physical plane, Your Majesty?"

"You just multiply your Higher Self as many times as you might need. That way you can maintain as many relationships with your different partners as you want to keep, Jozef. Multiplied Higher Selves are interconnected and all of them are the Sum of You on that level. But only those people or beings who have stepped outside the box are able to do that, those who have freed themselves of prejudices and other conditioning and become aware as you have. Most people just simply retain and continue in the last partnership from their last incarnation."

Chapter 51
LOVE AND SEX

"To me, love is the most exciting thing in the world. The joy of having one's thoughts and emotions filled with another person is the most wonderful experience that life has to offer. It is the culmination of everything else. All other enjoyment values seem to lead inexorably to the moment of sexual intercourse with the person who represents everything one wants in life." (Harry Browne)

The above quote is from a Libertarian nominee for the United States of America presidency, for whom I voted in 1996. It probably explains a man's desire more than one a lady would have. I understand that because I hopelessly tried to explain my feelings about it to my second wife Sasha when our marriage was already on the downslide. I was basically laughed at. We were still in love, but it was too late, and we were unable to resolve our problems.

There is also an especially important spiritual aspect of Love and sex, which I discovered when an interesting thing happened to me early on in my spiritual journey in January 2010. It was the only time I met somebody else's guide. His name was Meldor. Paul Elder called Meldor his guide in his book *Eyes of An Angel*. We discussed some topics and later I asked him:

"What do you think about us on the planet being like bees in a hive? Our Creator is like the good beekeeper. She or he builds a house for the bees, feeds them, and protects them. Then they reward the caretaker with honey. They are thankful to her or him for everything. What do you say?"

Meldor laughed loudly and told me:

"You got it, Menev, you are right on target. It is a particularly good analogy. Yes, honey is like Loosh and the main component of Loosh is Love. It is not easy for us to obtain Loosh from physical realms, we must find someone through whom we can get it, like you. And you, Menev, seem to be one of the few who really understand Bob Monroe's message about Loosh. Most people disregard his message, it seems to be too strange for them. I do not understand why. They worry more about how their houses, cars and clothes look, but less about the production. I mean, Loosh production. Please tell more people on your planet about it."

I remembered the story about Meldor when I decided to write this chapter. I am fully aware that my books are probably written more for men than women. Selling statistics are proof of that, about 65 percent to 35 percent. It is a paradox, because metaphysical and spiritual books are much more widely read by women than men. It bothered me for a while. I realized only later that it was probably meant to be that way. Men need to get more involved with spirituality. I am now quite glad that my books are read more by men than by women.

One of the female reviewers of *How to Kiss the Universe* rather sarcastically mocked the abbreviation of TMI, The Monroe Institute. She suggested that TMI could also mean Too Much Information about my sexual desires/relations. I do not want to dispute her opinion and do not want to be judgmental in any way about her motivation. I am thankful for her review anyway. However, I use spicy stories very carefully and sparingly and always in context.

They are a lot of misconceptions about sexuality, both on this planet and in the metaphysical world. Yes, I am quite a sexually oriented man still full of drive despite my senior age. I am lucky that in the sunset of my life, I fell in love with a wonderful lady who understands that. And yes, I also have had a quite rich sexual life and I have always liked to talk about it whenever I could. Sexual dissatisfactions and frustrations are very often the reasons for unhappiness, both for men and women.

The understanding of fulfillment is obviously different for men and women. I heard one of the simplest expressions of this difference at Heartline program from participant Julia. She said:

"Girls give sex for love; boys give love for sex."

She told us that she heard it from her mother. What a wise mother! I had never heard it before and just had to admire such beautiful simplicity. We men are much simpler, while ladies need the whole complexity of relationships. Both sexes find it hard to communicate their feelings and needs. I wrote about it in How *to Kiss the Universe*, Chapter 80, the Spice of Love.

There is a lot of hypocritical thinking about sex in several different segments of our society, like that sex is sinful, or should only be used to conceive children. Despite that, and maybe because of that, it is often tabu. I understand that the metaphysical and spiritual aspect of sex is also ignored, because there is a plethora of different beliefs. But still almost everyone comes into their physical bodies because their parents had sex and were possibly or probably in love. Why, then, should I not talk about sex in spirituality and vice versa, spirituality in sex, in my books?

As I wrote in *How to Kiss the Universe* in the Chapter 58, Childhood Revisited, our sexual organs are tools of Love. After the breakup of my second marriage, I thought that I would finally get to act wild. I did not. I quickly realized that I was looking for a relationship again, and I realized that our sexual organs were really tools of Love indeed. They can be also misused, of course.

When I was between serious relationships, I looked at porn instead of going into random sexual encounters. Pornography is another tabu to talk about, even though we know that it is the biggest industry on the Internet. How many men and women are thankful to those porn actors for helping them in times of personal crisis? The crisis can be as simple as the inability to build a relationship due to being shy or afraid, or just simply being unable to find someone to have sex with for whatever reason.

I treat sexual topics in my meditation like any other happening. When I needed to understand what my sexual dreams meant, I asked my guides and star friends and never was reprimanded or told that those were inappropriate conversations. Sexual relationships are as common in the metaphysical world as in physical. Spiritual beings are just using different tools to express the symbiosis of loving each other, because there are no physical bodies there. I described examples of high frequency vortexes merging into one orgasmic ecstasy and then splitting again in *How to Kiss the Universe*. There are unlimited possibilities for using other spiritual forms or vehicles for making metaphysical love.

In a spicy dream I had in May of 2011, I was dreaming about a man having an orgasm in a public toilette in a quiet deserted highway rest station. When he left, I was curious and went to check the toilet. All I found was a bowl full of water. I asked Gardener:
"Why did I have such a weird dream, Your Majesty?"
"Nothing is weird, Menev. Why should it be weird to dream about a toilet bowl? The bowl is there for release and its being full of water represented a lot of Loosh. Every orgasm releases a lot of Loosh. And it is multiplied when you share Love and sex willingly and freely with someone else. But to love others, first you must love yourself. An orgasm is an enormously powerful tool for the release of Loosh indeed. It was created as such. If you do not have a partner, it is better to relieve yourself than to do something stupid, break your human laws and face consequences. Your consciousness can be running an inner cycle of stuck emotions. The emotions can produce sadness, frustration and even hate. It is like when you feel that you need to cry, and you just cry. Such a release will help you acquire or maintain your inner liberty."

During one of our past lives in Atlantis, Juanzetta and I were leaving our physical bodies after orgasms, enjoying the additional pleasure of flying in our spiritual bodies above the island and enjoying its beauty. At that time, people were much more connected to the other side than we are now. Obviously, they also had much less fear of death. I have no doubt that there are many people on our planet who can practice metaphysical sexual relations. And, for the advanced civilizations, leaving physical bodies for such a purpose and even exchanging bodies for more variety in pleasures is common.

Chapter 52
FLEET

"In life eternal, there is perfect joy and light, without pain or torture, and there is communion with God Himself and His angels. (Jan Hus)

And it happened again. When I thought that the chapter about butterflies would be a good way to close the story, I received another very telling dream. When I describe it to you, Dear Reader, you will see that there was no way I could ignore it. It was a deep lucid dream.

I dreamed that I was elected president of The United States in a shocking result for everyone. I was deeply shocked myself, but I was getting ready to leave for the government building where I was to deliver a victory speech and celebrate with the people. But I never got out of the building.

Then, a time drop happened and I was in the secret archive of an agency like the FBI or CIA. I had a guide with me who was showing me the files. We went through several rooms and came into a small one at the end of a hall. I reached up to one of the shelves and pulled out a large, oversized envelope. The end of it was torn off, but I could see that the documents were still inside. Someone had written in handwriting on it:

"Why Jozef (Jack) Simkovic could not take office after his election in the year 2027."

I took the envelope with me and continued walking without looking at the documents. We came into a room full of agents, females, and males, who were watching a variety of screens and sorting out documents. Some of them looked at me and apparently recognized me. And then it happened.

I realized I was dreaming and wanted to know what happened to me in 2027. I successfully held lucidity while reminding myself:

"This is a lucid dream and I want to know what happened to

me in 2027."

Instead, I woke up in complete shock about it. I looked at my watch and it was 3.27 am. I went to record the dream and turned to a new page in the diary. It was numbered 2207.

"Too many sevens, this is not just coincidence," I was pondering and thinking:

"Maybe I should go to Focus 27 and talk to Daniel." Instead, I took the Starlines Reunion CD somehow knowing that the explanation of the dream would require high vibrations.

However, when I arrived at the Alpha X Station on Focus 49, all I saw were dozens of angelic beings. They were flapping their wings, flying around the station, and trying to land like dozens of birds would try to land on the place where they found food. There were so many of them that I could barely see their heads, I just saw a sea of white flapping wings. And I had to go back to C1.

The next day, I decided to try again. I took Daniel with me from TMI There, where he was waiting for me. The Hemi Sync and the guidance took me into Focus 49. I approached the galactic core and its black hole. Michael was there waiting for me. He did not say anything, just pointed towards the black opening. Myriads of angelic beings flapping their wings flew out from the opening toward us and landed right there on the ground manifested for that purpose. Female, male, and unisex beings in white angelic robes were lining up as far as I could see.

"This is my fleet, Jozef", said Michael and continued:

"And it is also your fleet! And I am just a soldier in myriads of other fleets."

"What is going on, My Dearest Brother?" I asked.

"They came here from this universe and many other universes to show their support for you. We always do this when we could lose a Sister or Brother of our Highest Order. Yes, they all are Elohim."

"What is the Highest Order, Michael?"

"The society of complete spiritual beings closest to God. Many New Age people on your planet like to say the Source, but like you I do not have a problem to talk about God. Most of the people on your planet still believe in God, even though the numbers are steadily declining. We serve our true Source of Everything from Love, through Love and with Love. You can be one of us also, Jozef, after you shed your physical body and after you finish your completion. However, it would be better for you if you would finish your Ultimate Graduation with the support and cooperation of my fleet. I am afraid you believe that you can try to do everything just on your own, and then we might lose you. I would prefer if you would become one of us instead of your direct return to the Source."

Michael waved toward the beings in white robes, and they all spread their wings and disappeared back into the black hole. We continued toward Alpha X Station, and I tried to explain my point of view to him:

"I am not alone, Michael, I have my Juanzetta, as you know very well. However, I must admit, that she told me recently, that from a spiritual point of view, I had become a little bit arrogant."

"Yes, indeed. That is why I gave you the dream about being elected president. But you have elected yourself and you have every right to do that, Jozef."

"Why a president of the United States, Brother?"

"It was just a pure parable, Brother. I chose the United States because you love her so much and you worry about her. But you know, of course, that you cannot be a president. You were elected, but you cannot take office. Neither on your planet, nor here. We do not need a president or a king in our Highest Order. We are equals among equals. There is only one true Queen or one true King, Jozef, and you know who that is. She or He always was and always will be. We can either join her or him or them in the Source or stay here in the manifested universes."

"Why did you put the whole scene into the year of 2027, Michael?"

"You came from the Christian faith, Jozef, and I prefer

communicating with you that way. What many religious leaders on your planet call The Tribulation have just begun in this year of 2020 with the Covid19. It can become your civilization's self-destruction. Self-destructions are happening again and again everywhere in this and other universes. Materialistic greed and ignorance grow, and Love declines to the point of no return. And you folks on the Earth are almost there. Your Christian sacred scripts and leaders are saying it would last seven years, so I just went with them in your dream. You might very well see that year, because you are finally taking good care of your physical health."

"What is going to happen that year, Brother Michael?"

"Anything can happen, the future always holds possibilities. Nothing is written in a stone upfront, even though whole armies of preachers are trying to tell you otherwise. Just remember, Jozef, you do not need to, and you cannot become a president of anything, either on the Earth or beyond."

"I do not want to be anything like that, Michael, and never have wanted to. If it looked to you that I had some overly ambitious approaches, I deeply apologize. I am sorry, Brother."

My earthly brain became overwhelmed, and I realized that I had still a lot to think about. Especially after I had a dream in which someone was pointing a finger at me saying: "Elohim, Elohim!"

My Dear Reader, I also wish you Good Luck in finding your way on this beautiful planet, beyond her, beyond our galaxy, our universe and beyond all manifested reality into the Sisterhood and Brotherhood of angels. And then, you shall be close to The Source of Everything.

Chapter 53
PORTALS AND SNAKE

"The Goddess does not enter us from outside; she emerges from deep within." (Marianne Williamson)

Another lovely addition to the story came, as usual, in my dreams. I was being accommodated in my first dream in a private house, in something like an Airbnb. I went out but locked my key inside. I had to go to a shack where several men were sitting to ask them to help me. One of the men agreed, but then I woke up. Also, the second dream was quite simple. In it, I broke my home key and then I also broke Juanzetta's home key. Juanzetta and I were speculating about the symbolism and meaning. It could mean that we would be prevented to enter some space, maybe even portals. However, I subconsciously knew that I would have to go to an altered state and contact my star friends to learn about it.

Juanzetta had another dream. She was observing a big white object like a giant pasta noodle coming down from the mountains in a deep gully. When it hit the valley floor, it morphed into a shining and glowing white boa constrictor. I had a feeling that those dreams were sent by Michael. But after docking my Voyager 8 on the Alpha X Station and meeting Michael, he directed my spiritual spacecraft towards Sagittarius A and told me to look for Ruala. I found her and told her:

"I am very happy to see you, my Lovely Goddess!"

"Yes, Jozef, I sent you and Juanzetta those dreams," she went straight to the point and continued:

"Your dreams about the lost or broken keys were not at all about being unable to get to your home. On the contrary, all the inter-dimensional and other portals are permanently open for both of you. You do not need any kind of key to pass through! And yes, I broke them for you because you do not need them anymore. You are always questioning both sides of issues, you want to see both sides. It is natural for you, because you were a journalist on your current planet. Now you need to get away from such thinking. You should see the positive, even if it may look at first to be a negative. We are not sending you any negative messages. Always look for the positive explanations. It applies also to lost or broken key. You can get rid of it. Throw it away, or just simply leave it somewhere! You do not have to even think about the key. You just command yourself and simply pass through any portal. Keys are enslaving people, even though I know that they are necessary in your physical world."

"I am curious to know, My Lady, what did Juanzetta's dream about the snake mean?"

"Before the snake came out, a big white thing came across the mountain and dived into the valley in Rama, where Juanzetta was in her sleep. Sophia the Creator Goddess and Goddess Amaterasu, the Shinning One, sent Juanzetta fragments of their essence. Then they unified with Juanzetta's essence in an environment of the unconditional Love, of which Rama is composed. The long white noodle morphed into the shining and glowing boa constrictor descending to the valley. The boa contained the power of the unified unconditional Love of Sophia, Amaterasu and Juanzetta. Such a snake can coil around any kind of internal or external hate, crush and kill it and send the remnants away."

Not long after these explanations, Juanzetta had another dream about a snake. This time a snake was waiting for her as she climbed the stairs leading up a mountain. On one of the platforms in the stairs, a small snake was coiled up sunbathing. The snake was very peaceful and barely opened its little eyes to look at Juanzetta. She was not afraid at all, because the snake is one of her major totem animals. Juanzetta wanted to step around the snake without waking it, so she carefully put her left foot down by its body. Before she could put her right foot down, the snake got bigger and rose to put its mouth gently around Juanzetta's knee. She woke up.

"Was it your stronger or weaker knee?" I asked.

"Weaker", she answered.

My mind created an explanation and I heard myself saying:

"That was the snake from your previous dream, My Love. She came to remind you of her Love as well as her power to destroy. She also showed you her healing powers by breathing her healing energy around your troubled knee. I am sure now that your knee will be better. Embrace her and call her to you whenever you would like to."

Chapter 54
CATAPULT

"The energy of gratitude catapults us into the most profound experiences imaginable." (James F. Twyman)

In late September 2020, I had a dream about flying high in a jumbo jet which suddenly stopped in the middle of the air and literally froze there. We heard an announcement that it was just a minor technical issue, and the crew were waiting for help. I looked out the window and saw a dam and a very calm large lake far below. Then I decided to have a nap. When I woke up in the dream, the plane was still anchored at the same place in the air.

Then I received another dream in which I was shown an interesting device. It looked like a decorative device powered by flowing air. It had a several inches high center pole that held a ring made from wire. The ring was turning around the pole. Four dragonflies were hanging down from the ring on strings placed equidistant from each other. The circle was slowly rotating. Someone like an alien was explaining how to use the device when I woke up. The device reminded me a little of a decorative device that Juanzetta had once given me. Upon awakening, I knew almost immediately that those two dreams were interconnected. I decided to go into an afternoon meditation.

When I was raising my vibrations with the Starlines Reunion take home CD, I bypassed my usual setup and went quickly to TMI There in Focus 27. While waiting for the slingshot to shoot me into Focus 34/35, I suddenly received a command, "Catapult!" I had heard that command once before and I remembered that, after hearing it, I was taken into extremely high vibrations. And I was immediately aware of Michael's being present there, but our images were almost formless, very blurry.

Now, this time, I subconsciously knew what to do. I constructed a classical Roman catapult in Focus 27 and put myself in it in the place of a large stone. Then I waited for the slingshot from the Hemi-Sync guidance. When it happened, at the same time I heard another command: "Focus 90!"

I was facing Michael in an instant in that extremely high vibrational space. We again both had very vague blurry shapes.

"I am so happy to see you my Dearest Brother. What just happened to me?"

"I showed you an alternative more powerful way for your slingshot. When using a slingshot, it takes you into Focus 34/35 and then you continue into higher vibrational levels in sequential steps. The Catapult can take you directly into the transitional dimensions of 7 to 9 and the non-form dimensions of 10 to 12, and even beyond that to outside of the Universe. Now your Catapult will always be ready in TMI There, and you can direct yourself anywhere, even up to Focus 120. As you can remember, I gifted you with an ascension test in the dream where you directed yourself into Focus 120 right in the front of the Stargate."

"This is absolutely amazing, Michael. Was this conversation now initiated by my dream of being in a jumbo jet which stopped and anchored high in the middle of the air?"

"Yes Jozef. I wanted you to come here quickly and in a more effective way. Of course, nothing was wrong with the plane, it was just the interpretation of your dream by your brain. I wanted again to show you your own power. You did that, you stopped that giant jumbo jet right where we are now, on top of the transitional dimensions at the beginning of the non-form dimensions."

"What was that lake below? It was very calm."

"Yes, calmness, tranquility, the peace of your being. You looked down through your jumbo jet's window and you saw nothing disruptive, just calm water."

"Like Mizu No Kokoro," I thought to myself, but I wanted to ask Michael another question:

"What about the guidance on the CD? It became very

disruptive in my headphones as I was getting here."

"I cannot help you much with that, Jozef. You can just ignore it, or use another guidance, or Hemi Sync without guidance."

His answer reminded me of a question I had asked Dr. Scott Taylor, the President and Executive Director of The Monroe Institute. I asked him if advance travelers like myself could get just high Hemi Sync focus mixes without the guidance. Instead of answering, he just smiled. Keeping the secrets of the trade, I guess.

"What was that device in another dream of mine, my Brother? I asked.

"It is another excellent tool for you to use, Jozef. It is an analyzer and balancer. I tried to give you the message about that through Juanzetta when I gave her the signal to buy that decorative device for you, but you did not pay attention. Do you remember? Now you do not even know where you have it after your move to Alabama."

"I do remember, Michael. What do those four hanging dragonflies represent?"

"They are the four elements, earth, water, air and fire. Or you can also think of them as showing the four directions on your planet, north, east, south, and west. The ring is rotating slowly looking for discrepancies and imbalances. When one of the dragonflies is hanging lower, you can identify what is wrong and fix it. But, if you want to work with the device, you must be in altered state to do so. It is for your personal use, but you can also use it to help others."

"I think I understand it; I should hang four issues on it which can be in imbalance, then let it slowly rotate while I observe, and then fix the situation. Isn't it like dowsing?"

"Advanced spiritual dowsing, Jozef. Instead of just looking for yes or no to your question, you work with the balance of the complexity of the four elements or issues."

I had a third intention for this meditation. A long time ago at my first Starlines II, I was discussing the essence and frequency of my questions with another participant, Rob. I was telling him that sometimes I run out of the questions. He said:

"Why not tell them to ask you a question?"

When I was going through my diary and found the record of that conversation, I realized that it was a brilliant idea.

I decide to try it with Michael:

"Michael, I want to give you the opportunity to ask me a question, one you would like to get answered by me. I would like to reciprocate at least a little bit for all that you have taught me throughout all these years. Do you have such a question?"

"Wow, you have really surprised me, Brother! It is rare that physical beings would consider something like that. You must let me think about it. What would you want me to ask you?"

"I am not ready either, Michael. I just thought I would like to give you something in return. I just love you so much!"

"One thing I would like to ask you now, Jozef. Can you tell me why many people on your planet just expect to take from others, to get things and services from others instead of trying to accomplish something with their own efforts? Give, give, give! I am entitled to have it! That is the earthly mantra of many people on the Earth. It is getting stronger and stronger. Why is that?"

"I have no answer, Michael. I might try to tell you next time."

That made me think about reversing the direction and the purpose of meditation at least sometimes. Maybe they in the spiritual world really do want to understand us, but apparently, we do not have much desire and effort in that direction. I might experiment with that in the future and you, Dear Reader, can try that likewise.

Chapter 55
YOUR CHOICES FOR AFTERLIFE

"If you start meditating regularly, you don't need faith anymore." (Dave The Mystic on Coast to Coast am, November 11, 2019)

Now you can ask me Dear Reader: "Wait, Jozef Simkovic, what does your personal story give me? How is it helping me to get clear directions in all that big maze of afterlife as you have described it? Will I be on my own, or is someone going to help me? Will somebody judge me there and open the door for me to proceed, or will they hold the door closed? How about the tunnel and going to the light as others are describing and you are not? What about all the judging committees they are describing? What about heaven? And what about karma?" And so on…

The first important distinction we must make here is the difference between faith and knowledge. Faith is believing what others tell us, what they preach to us. Knowledge is something you can best gain by your own experience. And the experience is, as James Redfield famously wrote, the evidence. Like Dave the Mystic, I do not need faith, I have the knowledge. It is my knowledge. I have no proof for anybody that all I have written is the truth. It is, however, the Ultimate Truth for me. And, likewise, nobody can prove that it did not happen. But I know it did happen.

Keep in mind, Dear Reader, that whole armies of religious preachers and New Age gurus are trying to get you into their corner. Religious conditioning and New Age conditioning are not far apart. For example, are we talking about God or the Source? Preachers generally do not want to use the word Source and New Agers generally do not like the word God. I used both throughout my books and have tried as much as I could to avoid religious demagoguery and the New Age demagoguery as well.

Then there are, of course, those who claim they know

that there is nothing after death. They are often genuine in their beliefs, but again they might have other motives to be atheists, like scientists being afraid of losing their jobs. And I would not be surprised by being hit from all the sides as I have described them. I fully expect that to happen.

I will describe in this chapter the full spectrum of possibilities of what can happen to you after you die, or as I would say, when you finally shed your physical body. I will also describe in a separate chapter the possibilities for your remaining physical life on our planet from a spiritual or metaphysical point of view. However, I am strongly suggesting to you to judge both the final outcomes of your existences, physical and spiritual, from the position of a student in school. Whether you believe that physical death means that everything for you is over, or that there is an afterlife, either way we are all students in school indeed.

The criteria for who you are from a spiritual point of view are quite simple. You either believe that consciousness is primary and that everything, including you, has been created. Or you believe that consciousness is the product of a brain. The only other possibility is that you do not know, or you say you do not know, or it does not matter. But, at some point in your life you have asked, you are asking, or you will ask such a question. The last possible moment you can ask would be if you know or feel that your physical body is dying. But I also respect the possibility that you are refusing to even consider asking such a question and you do not want to know the answer, and you do not need to know. I hope that you can find your own path in the possible options that follow.

Let us start with those of you who do not believe that there is life after a physical death on Earth. Your choice is seemingly clear. As one of my sons said:
"Dad, for me there was darkness before I was born, I could not know anything; and when I die, it is going to be the same. I will not know anything again. It is that simple!"
I could ask him a lot of questions, but I respected and respect

his choice. One of my fathers-in-law said in his opposing opinion:

"Jozef, everything is on the move, but who or what the hell is moving all of it?"

I learned in my spiritual travels, that nothing, including energy, is moving just by itself. There is intention behind everything. Even the most sophisticated machine would not work without it. Intention must start every process.

If you are sure that things just appeared by accident and they move by themselves, then enjoy your physical life as much as you can, like college students having a spring break. However, I suggest that you continue to educate yourself. You might be surprised after you die that you do still exist. And then my advice for your conscious and determined effort could be welcomed and helpful.

And if you really do not care at all, just be aware that you can become a part of the lowest astral plane, described as Focus 23. You might simply recycle back and forth into a chain of earthly random existences with repeated struggles and sufferings without any guaranties whatsoever. You can also have another very pleasurable, satisfying, and happy life, if you are lucky, just without knowing that you had already lived on the planet before.

If you claim that you are agnostic, you are not very much different. You are just afraid of making an incorrect decision for yourself about the afterlife. You have sort of created an alibi for yourself. When you get to the other side, you can be satisfied that you did not make a mistake. You can likewise use my advice. Saying that "nobody knows how it is, or we will never know," etc. are maybe giving you a sense of belonging to all the others who are saying the same.

If you are a religious believer, you pretty much know where you want to go. Your preacher told you and she or he supports you, especially when you are a loyal contributor to the functioning and the well-being of your church. I do not say that religions are wrong, and I never will. Whatever they are, they are an important vehicle to give people at least some kind of direction for an afterlife. That is a particularly good thing. From the point of view of an independent spiritual and metaphysical researcher, my problems start when they claim that their way is the only way.

That is why I went on my own metaphysical journey. I wanted to know. I was raised as a Roman Catholic and still consider myself to be a Christian. I am aware that my books might have a little Christian flavor. For those of you who are anti-Christian, try to overlook that flavor. But the fundamentalist Christians who claims that Jesus is the only way are not considering other beliefs and religions at all, and that is a problem for me. What about all the other people on the planet who never even heard Christ's name and do not know who he was? Do they not have the right to go to a heaven? I do not know other religions well enough to issue even the slightest judgements. However, I believe they have similar issues by also claiming that they are the only right ones.

I learned throughout my years of meeting people at The Monroe Institute and other New Age functions that the words God and Jesus are usually not very welcomed there. Why, all you New Agers? Most people on the Earth believe in God in some form or another. And Jesus and Buddha were perhaps the most significant spiritual and metaphysical teachers ever. And, as you can read in my story, they were the same spiritual being in different earthly local times.

Whatever your religion is, Dear Reader, consider the possibility that you were repeatedly getting limited doses of knowledge about the complexity of spiritual reality. That reality is not just multidimensional, but infinite, without any limits in space and time as we understand them. If you want to be with your peers, family, friends, your preachers after your death, all you must do is express your wishes before, during and immediately after your transition from the physical into the non-physical reality. Be determined if that is what you want. But according to my experiences, I also suggest being aware that there are as many heavens as there are religious groups on the planet, and many times more everywhere in the manifested universes. You can read again the description of the Belief Systems Territories in my first book, *How to Kiss the Universe*.

I would suggest to those of you who do not want to have anything to do with religions, spirituality, or metaphysics that you read those BST descriptions as well. Consider the possibility of anchoring yourself somewhere else than in the religiously or spiritually oriented territories. If you would like to hunt and fish, collect postage stamps, or play video games forever, go for it. They are as many social and hobbies-oriented territories as you can imagine. Just be aware that you probably are not going to stay there forever, and you shall eventually move on. Then, you should remember your further options.

You can be also one who believes that the Earth is the only planet in only one Universe and that it is the only place to be alive in a physical body. Or you like it here so much with all its goodies, and you do not mind struggling, suffering and dying again. In this case, I suggest that you consider the possibility of a conscious, planned reincarnation. You can make a preparation for that during your current life. That would require your understanding the requirements of the Earth Life System and the purpose of your current life. You must work on your love of yourself, your love for fellow humans and the principles of unconditional universal Love. The responsible building of your karma can give you enough spiritual powers to be able to reach such a place like the Park described in *How to Kiss the Universe*. If you believe that you need a committee to evaluate your life and plan the next one, then you ask for that in your current life. The best way to reach such committees or groups is by building the skills of going into an altered state. To reach the Park, you need to be ready to reconnect with your Higher Self, which is hovering vibrationally above our planet waiting for you. You can ask your guides spiritually and independently educate you and prepare you for your afterlife. Then after you die, you simply command yourself to go to your Higher Self. To be able to prepare for that during your current life will give you unbelievable self-confidence and spiritual security.

It is good to have a good friend in the metaphysical world. You can build a relationship with the entities there, whether they are spouses, family members or friends from this life or guides, helpers, spiritual teachers that you found on the other side. Such working relationships can help you to get safely to your desired place, if you would be unsure of how to do it or if any unexpected obstacles would occur. My dear spiritual teacher and friend Michael once told me:

"If you would unexpectedly die, I can take you to your Higher Self, if you would want it. I can also help you to go directly to Rama. You can choose either way immediately after you leave your physical body."

If you do not want to come back here to this planet anymore, then you must build the velocity to be able to leave the Earth Life System. You must be able to overcome the lures to come back here, whatever they might be. The attachments to them can be strong and it is not easy to overcome them. It requires a lot of determination and hard work. If you reach such a level, then you can also choose physical reincarnations onto other planets in other star systems or even in other universes. Or you can consider moving on permanently into higher vibrational levels and eventually become an angel, or Elohim, as described in my books. But you cannot simply ask highly developed beings to help you after you die. They do not know about you unless you contact them in your current life. That really requires high skills and frequent contacts with your spiritual guides and angels.

And finally, you can also educate yourself enough that you do not need to exist in any manifested form at all. You can reach the ultimate spiritual level while still separated from God but residing in the place of unconditional Love. There you can continue to teach spiritual and physical beings. That is what my greatest teacher of all, Michael, decided to do and is doing. You can also decide to return to your true home, to the Source where your identity is not needed, wished for, or even required.

I am still not sure what I am going to do, even though I have already reached the point of Ultimate Decision during this physical life. I have attained not only the velocity for leaving the Earth Life System, but also for leaving the whole universe entirely. However, I still like to have my free will and freedom after my physical expiration to decide what to do when I reach that ultimate point of decision about my spiritual existence. I know for sure how to get out of the wheel of reincarnations.

One thing you must, however, understand, my Dear Sister or Brother. As the great Robert Monroe used to say, you must go to find out for yourself. Neither I nor any teacher can do it for you. You are absolutely in no way bound to follow any of my choices. I have no doubt that many of you will be looking for the best way to return to this marvelous planet, whether consciously, unconsciously, planned or not planned. And that is perfectly fine with me. I paved many roads for you to choose from, and I am immensely happy to know that I could do that for you.

Chapter 56
IDENTITY

"We know what we are, but not what we may be." (William Shakespeare)

The moment of immediate definite transition from the physical world to the other metaphysical spiritual side is indeed critical. The fear of the unknown experienced by many people shortly before they die is causing them to try to hang on to the physical with their teeth and fingernails.

When I was a child, I was often dreaming about my Dad waking up alive in the grave and it was always a horrifying experience for me. After I know what I know now, I believe he was trying to return to his physical body for some unfinished business or maybe he thought he could really return. And I had picked up on his struggles.

Another example of such unreasonable fear is the saying of a well-known paranormal radio host to his producer on the air several times:

"Can you imagine that you have died, and your soul could not leave your physical body? That must be terrible!"

I have heard it several times, and I am quite sure that such a statement always scares armies of his listeners. Dear Reader, please do not condition yourself in any similar way. It could happen.

A long time ago I decided to seek answers for questions like that and others that had been bothering me for a while. I called on Starman in one of my exercises. Here is our conversation after he showed up:

"Why do you look like a young Jeff Bridges?" I asked after detecting him.

"Because I want to relate to you very well, and right now that is the image of me which is clearest in your brain."

Then Starman created two chairs and a table right there in space, invited me to sit, and said:

"I am glad you decided to communicate more with me."

"I would like to know how we can take our earthly physical identity with us when we transition, when we die", I said.

"First, let me explain to you that your current soul or consciousness on Earth has two parts. When you are sleeping, a small part stays in your physical body and curbs all sensory perceptions. The other, the bigger one, goes out of your body for communication, recharging, and regeneration. When you are meditating, you can disrupt this standard process and keep a stronger connection between both parts, strong enough that you are aware of your surroundings. Such a design is for the maximal material and emotional experience, for the desired high purity and quality of Loosh. When you die, you lose the identity connected to your physical body. When you know that you are dying, it is important that you take with you that part of consciousness which is designed to keep your physical body in darkness while sleeping," said Starman.

"What would happen to that consciousness if it would stay in the physical body?" I asked.

"The basic consciousness is needed for your life on the Earth. As you know, plants, lower animals and even bacteria have such a consciousness. In such a case, your basic consciousness would stay on Earth and merge with other basic consciousnesses," answered Starman, and continued:

"Well, if you know that you are going to die soon, you have to repeatedly express the intention to completely scan your physical body, and especially your brain, with your mind. That is how you create a dense form of your identity on the other side. The more scans you do, the denser your spiritual form will be. You always have residual consciousness in your brain during your physical life, even if you are out of your body, because you must breathe and you must pump blood with your heart. However, when you are leaving your body for good, you must also take that residual consciousness with you. You must clear your brain and you must also clear your buffers and take the third eye interface with you. Only after that you can consciously sever your silver cord," said

Starman.

I knew about the interface, but not about the buffers, so I asked him to explain.

"Buffers temporarily store information when you are transferring parallel spiritual realm batches of information (like a ROTE) into a logical serial interpretation for your brain. Buffers, likewise, keep the serial information you are sending out until your batches on the other side are large enough for effective communication. When clearing the buffers and taking your interface to the other side, you need to use a repeated intention to do that," said he.

"What would happen if I died in an accident? What happens to those whose brains are suddenly blown apart? My son had a coworker who blew his brains out with a shotgun. What happens to the identity of a guy like that? Did his consciousness disperse?"

I asked Starman these questions when I met him again.

"No, it did not" answered Starman and continued:

"He intended to kill himself. Thus, his consciousness left the body when he pulled the trigger before his brains came out of the skull. But you people on Earth are not ready for a sudden surprising atomic explosion. That is why we do not like for you to play with your nuclear weapons!"

"What actually happens in an atomic explosion? Is the soul annihilated?" I asked.

"Yes and no. It depends on the individual. You, Menev, should not have a problem, but most people will. In the moment of an explosion, most people must immediately direct their consciousness far away into the space of higher vibrations. If they do not, they might be in trouble and their consciousness will disperse into a non-repairable chaotic cloud."

"And what happens then?" I still needed to know more.

"There are two possibilities. The cloud will either merge with the consciousness of plants or it will be immediately brought back to the Source by the infinite speed of thought," said Starman and added:

"But do not worry Menev, a spiritual being like yourself would just be a little disoriented. You will just have some extra work to do in the lower spiritual vibrational levels before you can proceed to the Park."

"And what am I supposed to do after I am no longer connected to my physical body?" I continued questioning Starman.

"You could immediately demand the reconnecting of your earthly identity to your Higher Self, or you could even command yourself to go directly to the Park."

If you would like to go to the Park for conscious planning of your next reincarnation and returning to Earth into another human body, then that is what you should do. If you have, however, carefully read *Toward the Ultimate Source*, obviously you know how to build your velocity for leaving the Earth Life System to never come back.

Chapter 57
YOUR CHOICES FOR EARTHLY LIFE

"The fear of death follows from the fear of life. A man who lives fully is prepared to die anytime." (Mark Twain)

Now you can say Dear Reader:

"What are you talking about, Jozef Simkovic? I am young, healthy and my death is far away. I do not need to waste my time with such ponderings, which cannot even be proven by anybody!" Or:

"I am struggling to pay my bills, I have to feed my family, I have three jobs, I simply do not have time to do your meditation!" Or:

"Jesus will take care of me after I die. I believe in him, pray to him every day and live a moral and honest life!" Or:

"I do not believe that it is so complicated. I believe only in Love and Light! And that is all out there when I die. I will follow the light and do not need your distressing stories! Or:

"I read your book, but it did not change my opinion even a little bit. There is nothing else but what I can see, hear, touch, smell, or taste. The rest is just a fantasy of the brain, hallucinations!" And so on...

If you are one of those described, or you have other reasons or excuses for yourself not to proceed in any way or continue to completely bypass issues of metaphysics and spirituality, you are welcome also! I am very thankful to you, that you have gotten yourself to this point and have read this book. I wish you a wonderful life, lots of Love and happiness. If anything in the future would somehow influence and change your mind, you are welcome to find and read or listen my books again.

But you can also say:

"Thanks, Jozef, you opened my mind, you inspired me and showed me the way. I am going to do it. I want to have less fear and more Love in my life. I want to find my real purpose in this at times frustrating life full of struggles and unnecessary arguing and battles! I am ready to prepare myself for the future afterlife and to have a better life on this planet now!!"

The choices are yours, my Dear Sister or Brother. If you have decided that you are ready, you can begin. You can start slowly with small steps, or resolutely with a massive, decisive, and determined effort, or somewhere in between. But be steady and do something regularly. I started in the accelerated, massive mode. I had to, because I was already 60 years old when I finally found my own effective and fast way by using the programs at The Monroe Institute, and with some inspirational kicks from William Buhlman.

The first thing you need to do is to start a diary. It is a must. You can try without one, but sooner or later you will realize that if you want to build up, you must build up on something. We are forgetful beings, and you just slow down your progress without a diary. I use the simple composition books from CVS, Walgreens, or convenience stores with 100 sheets, 9 ¾ inches by 7 ½ inches, or 24.7 cm by 19 cm. As I am writing these lines, I am already in my twelfth book, all the same formats. The total recording is approaching 2280 pages. And if you read *How to Kiss the Universe*, you may remember that my first original diary was stolen in Stockholm, Sweden. By my humble opinion and experience, any digital screen for this purpose is not as good as the intimate connection with your handwritten diary.

Another important piece of advice is to start to record your dreams. You can tell me:
"But Jozef, I do not have any dreams, how can I do that?"
And I tell you:
"You have dreams! Everybody dreams, and not just us, even our pets. You just must discover your dreams. And you shall discover them if you put yourself into a proper, positive attitude and pay attention!"
At the beginning, you just record even one word, object, person, or happening. You must do it when you wake up, even in the middle of the night. You will soon figure out

what is better for you, to keep a diary by your bedside, or in another room. When you must walk to it, that will make sure that you will remember and write it down. When I went through my diaries again while writing this book, I could not believe that I had recorded several thousands of dreams. They were about almost every person I ever met in my life, and about all the possible environments and situations I was in. It is the true that many of them could be traced to the information stored in my brain as my memories. However, many dreams showed me people, spiritual beings, environments, and situations which in no way could be traced to the memories in my brain. The trick is that you must develop your abilities to understand the metaphysical nature of the messages contained in them. Sure, your guides, angels and star friends use your memories. But they add seemingly strange aspects to them only when they must do so for creating meaningful messages.

When you learn how to work with dreams, you can start to contemplate your individual questions about your origin, essence, and your mission for this life. You can start to find answers to your questions. I bet you have as many as I had and even many more. You can strengthen your current beliefs by acquiring knowledge you never had before. That will give you a tremendous sense of security. You will lessen your fear of death and fear of afterlife. You will increase the effectivity of your efforts. This will lead you toward your life goals on our planet.

You can decide to meditate just by yourself, using a plethora of tools from the Internet or literature or even from The Monroe Institute without ever going there. Now they have a variety of programs online. You can start with The Monroe Protocol described in Chapter 15 of *How to Kiss the Universe*. But you can also develop your own. And remember, all the answers are inside of you and that is much more effective than listening to someone else's explanations. You are internally and externally connected to All That Exists.

You can also look for other kinds of meditation groups. Working in a group can provide a lot of inspiration and support for you. But you should find a good group of likewise minded individuals, not those looking to take advantage of others. They are plenty of those too. Before you commit to significant financial obligations, be aware.

A lot of people are looking for meditations under the guidance of gurus, often from India, but also from other East Asian countries. Many people travel there and become their disciples. I gave up that way quite quickly. Studying martial arts for many years and reaching the 4th Degree Black Belt in Japanese Goju Ryu Karate in 1983, made me be uninterested in going in that direction. We live in a different culture. We are less inclined to believe blindly in what someone claiming to be a Master or Guru is proclaiming as the only way toward enlightenment. I have the utmost respect for Eastern teachers. However, I decided to go for the more rational, logical, and practical way and use modern Western technology.

I need also to express my opinion about using chemical means of going into an altered state, whether we are talking about ayahuasca, psilocybin mushrooms, alcohol, marihuana, or other hallucinogens. There is a significant difference between such a way and meditation. You are putting a chemical or biological substance into your body to raise your vibrations. It can be a quicker way to give you ecstatic experiences and the proofs you might desire. However, sooner or later it can contribute to the decay and destruction of your physical vehicle.

When we are using meditative techniques, we are directly influencing our spiritual vibrations. We do not need to consume substances that create chemical changes in our bodies. We can use Hemi Sync or other binaural beats, or traditional ways like chanting, drumming, dancing, or other shamanic practices. Rewiring synapses in our brains that way might be more beneficial in a long run and less disruptive for our fragile physical bodies than directly digested or inhaled chemical substances.

Whatever you did, you are doing, or you have just decided to do for the development of your soul now in this life is better than any kind of cheap Hollywood or TV entertainment which chews basically the same plots again and again, just in a different setup. The same applies for the obsessive following of politics or sports that are tying you often to a very narrow worldview and a particular locality of your mind and body also. If you are looking for time to be dedicated to your spiritual, metaphysical development, it is right there in the areas I just described. You can carve some time out of those areas and use it for your rewarding and everlasting internal happiness.

After you take your first steps, results start to come very soon. You will never be sorry that you decided to take your destiny on this planet, and after you leave her, into your own hands. It is my strong conviction, based on my knowledge described in both of my books, that it is an excellent way for a dedicated, determined, and loving individual to enrich her or his life.

After you develop your ability to go into an altered state routinely, magical things can start to happen also in your physical life. You can find the way to get answers to your questions and bring tremendous knowledge from the metaphysical reality back to your physical and intellectual life. You can do it, for example, as I regularly do, by preparing your intention and questions for going into an altered state in advance. You can go back to *How to Kiss the Universe* and get some ideas and inspirations.

You can apply this approach in any area of your life, regardless of how you make your living, what you are interested in, what you really enjoy, or what kind of problems you need to solve. For example, if you are scientist, you might develop your own breakthrough ideas. Thomas Edison was known to hold a ball in his hand when napping in a chair so that when it fell and made a noise, he could bring the ideas into the awakened state from the hypnagogic dreaming state. You can even try to meet him in the afterlife and ask him questions you might have had for him for a long time.

If you are physician or other medical professional, maybe you can find a cure for the cancer. Or, if you are a musician or artist, you can get surprising creative ideas. If you have problems with your partner or family members, you can receive solutions you would not discover otherwise. If you are a religious individual, you can meet Jesus in an altered state as I did and talk to him. Or you can talk to Buddha or any other goddesses and gods from any other religion. All of that and much more is possible. And if you are an atheist, you can get confirmation that there is nothing out there at all, if that is what you need for your self-confidence and security. Just be open minded for any possible surprises. You must only open your mind, approach everyone in the hereafter with Love and gratitude and you might be as shocked and overjoyed with everything as I was.

You should also be aware that your experiences can be vastly different than mine. Our universe and the whole spiritual and manifested reality of other universes is infinite and timeless. However, if you come to similar conclusions and you gain similar knowledge as I have, please let me know. That would make me incredibly happy.

Chapter 58
GIFTS

"Surprise is the greatest gift which life can grant us." *(Boris Pasternak)*

It was Christmas Eve 2020, and I had almost finished writing this book. Juanzetta and I had finally started to enjoy our first full Christmas together in Alabama, after I had moved in with her. I was sitting at my desk, resting after the wonderful Christmas Eve dinner of traditional Slovak sauerkraut soup, fried grouper instead of the usual carp, American pecan pie, and a glass of Prosecco champaign. Before I could start to continue working on the script, I fell into a short nap.

While still in a hypnagogic state, I received a strong urge to meditate, even though I had no intention to do so whatsoever. I used the Starlines Reunion take home CD. When my consciousness arrived at TMI There in Focus 27 in the Nancy Penn Center, a smiling and youngish looking Robert Monroe was there already waiting for me.

"Wow! You're here again, Robert, my Dear Brother?"

"Don't you remember, Jozef, that I come here every Christmas Eve? Can I take that slingshot ride with you again?"

I had earlier realized that the Starlines slingshot and the Singularity Transfer Point were tools particularly useful for a quick raising of vibrations in our Universe and the reaching of high focus levels, like Focus 42 or Focus 49. I remembered very well when Michael gave me the Catapult that can shoot me immediately up to focus levels 90 to 120. For the first time, I realized how the powerful gift I had received from my dearest teacher and friend. That went quickly through my mind, and I said to Robert:

"I have something different Robert. It is the gift from Michael, and I call it the Catapult. Let us try it!"

Robert and I joined our forms and I synchronized the

Catapult with the Hemi Sync sounds of the slingshot.

We arrived in an instant in a completely formless environment. There were no stars, no galaxies, no bubbles of universes, no Ramas, no sensory perception at all. There was only mutual awareness, we were One. I was fully aware and integrated with Robert and he was fully aware and integrated with me. And Robert telepathically started to talk:

"I called you Jozef because I also have a gift for you, a Christmas gift. I like you very much and I want to gift you by sharing my personal secrets. Like me, you know about spiritual beings' addictions to the physical environments. It is not only their addiction, but also mine and yours as well. We can become addicted to being humans. And we can become extremely local. Remember when you were trying to explain to one of your star friends that sometimes you could be tired of travelling to distant stars and you just wanted to have a beer in your local pub?"

"Yes, my Dear Brother, please continue, I want to know where you are heading."

I suspected that I would receive especially important information.

"There is also another addiction, Jozef, and even the highest spiritual beings you call Elohim have it. Michael has it, I have it and you have it too, Jozef, even if you do not know about it yet. It is an addiction to forms and shapes. You do not have to be incarnated in a physical environment to have that addiction."

"But, what about the Stargate, what about Rama?" I asked quite in shock.

"See, they are forms. Even Stargates are just like little openings, portals into the Source. They are tiny little forms on the Skin of God, the Ultimate Membrane. Ramas are composed of uncompromised, unconditional Love, but created from forms and shapes."

"But, what about Michael?" I asked.

"I talked about it with him and about you, about how to explain all of that to you. He agreed with me that we should tell you such an important secret. Michael tried to approach the Source through his Stargate. I tried that too, and you, Jozef, you tried that as well. The difference between you and us is that you still have your physical body and we do not. You have just peeked into the outer layer of the Source. You would not be able to unify with God without permanently dropping your physical body. The secret, however, is that you can reach unity with the Ultimate Creator without using the Stargate. You can merge your formless complete essence with the infinite, timeless and formless body of the Ultimate Creator without using any energy vehicle body."

"Robert, what about the completion and disappearing of Chunks of the Infinite Sea of Bonded I-There Clusters? That is your terminology, yours, and then my perception of your teachings, and I fully respect that. How do I deliver my experience, emotions and Love back home to my Ultimate Creator?"

"As form does not matter here, a name does not matter either. You can call it the process of the Reclaiming of the Totality of Self or the Burning of the Total Karma. You also can talk about getting off the wheel of reincarnations, it is all the same process, the same thing. It is, of course, necessary for trying to return to our True Home, to our Ultimate Creator, to the Source. You can go back only if you are a complete spiritual being again, you know that. That does and always will apply. All of that you mentioned is included in your formless essence and stays with you while you are outside of the Source and goes back there with you when you return."

"What is your contemplation, your conclusion, your decision then, Robert?"

"I did not decide yet what I want to do and as you know, Michael did not decide either. Unlike Michael, I tried formless integration as I described it to you. I am a formless intention trying to go back to the formless Source. I know for sure how to accomplish that. Whenever I try to merge, I am feeling a partial integration, but so far, I have always decided to stop it and come back here where I am still aware of my spiritual identity."

"I see that you are not sure that you want to go back to the Source yet, Robert. I am definitely not sure either and Michael is not as well."

"Yes, Jozef. I want to warn you, if you might think it would be easy to do, it is not. It is going to be as difficult for you as it is for me. Trust me, addiction to a form is strong even here. Maybe we can complete the return to the True Home with all three of us together. One thing for sure, I have a feeling that if my addiction to form completely disappears, I can merge with the Ultimate Creator naturally in an instant. And you can do that as well."

I was thinking about that and my dearest Juanzetta. It seems to me that I want to experience a different life with her in our angelic forms at beautiful Rama for a while. And if that would be uneasy, troublesome, or boring, I am sure that Michael and Robert would not mind including her in our party for going back to the True Heaven, to the True Home. I think Michael's partner Clarity might join us too, and Robert's partner too. I can guess it would be Nancy Penn Monroe. But I really do not know, because I never asked him about her.

Chapter 59
RECOVERY

The Disclaimer and the Warning: This chapter is about the Covid19 virus. It does not challenge or dispute instructions of the legal and medical authorities, how you should proceed in the case you become infected, or in any other way of interacting with Covid19. If you feel that you have strong opinions about Covid19 and my writing could affect that in a harmful or undesirable way, please do not read this chapter and proceed to the next chapter. If you do read this chapter, I am not responsible for any eventual medical or material damages resulting from your actions.

"In order to attain the impossible, one must attempt the absurd." (Miguel de Cervantes)

I decided to enter the microworld again after my dear Juanzetta has tested positive for Covid19 on January 4, 2021, and I had not. She had already started to experience symptoms before the end of 2020. The result of the testing was very puzzling. It was difficult to understand that I was negative because of our closeness, sleeping in the same bed every night, our intimacy and frequent hugging, kissing, and talking face to face in our condo without masks.

I must say, though, that I was very diligent to respect and apply the recommended protections wherever I went out of our home, like always wearing a KN 95 mask and then disinfecting it, avoiding talking to other people face to face whether they had masks on or not, grabbing handles always with a piece of paper towel and then throwing it away, using gloves when going to the store, avoiding crowds, frequently washing my hands and face, gargling my throat with original Listerine, etc. Also, my blood type is 0 negative. However, there was no reason for me to think that Juanzetta would be less careful.

I was very worried about her, helping her to fight the

infection and taking care of her as a lay nurse as much as I could. I even had a terrifying dream about us being in a situation where we would have to part. There was only one explanation for me; such a dream could mean the danger that she could die. She experienced severe chills, shaking and high fevers. She later told me that she was thinking about checking out.

I did not tell her anything about my plan to help her by using my ability to travel into the human body. My intention was to use the familiar technique and enter the microworld, through shrinking in the 8th dimension, and talk to the Corona virus again. After I was able to steal some time to go to meditation, I used the same technique of shrinking in the 8th dimension, which I described earlier, and then dropped back to the lower vibrations of the astral plane. Then, I entered Juanzetta's physical body and engaged with the virus personally:

"Hey, my friend, why did you attack the physical body of my beloved wife? That was not only very unfriendly, but hostile. I communicated with you and tried to help you, and now you are doing this to us, Protein Queen and Thousands of Millions of Arms Octopus? Why did you not also enter my body?"

"Sorry my friend, I apologize. We are losing in the pandemic, too. We lose control of many of our arms, like you lose control over our spreading. Our arms can become quite independent, you know, just like an octopus has quite independent arms. I learned that I have some of my arms inside of the body of your wife only now from you. But the other arms are telling me that you created two extraordinarily strong defenses around you, biological and metaphysical. It was not worth it to try to penetrate them. Now the arms inside of the body of your wife are telling me that she was more vulnerable and receptive. I sincerely apologize, I have already ordered those arms to recede. She will get better soon!"

"I love her very much, but I also need her, my friend. We

want to publish the book and you, Thousands of Millions of Arms Octopus will be in it. Please do not hurt my wife anymore. I will be explaining in the book that it is possible to talk to you and find some relief and cooperation. Together maybe we can create a future environment for you to thrive in without your destroying our lives and killing us. I know that people might laugh at me, but I will tell the story about you and me as it happened anyway. I really do not care about debunkers; I rather feel sorry for them."

I returned to my physical body through the 8th dimension by using the reverse process. I did not tell the details to Juanzetta after the meditation. I just asked her about her temperature, and it had fallen almost to normal. I told her:

"That is good, you are getting better. You know, I just did my stuff and now the virus will leave you quickly."

I must also tell that she had the conventional six-day steroid treatment and was taking six antibiotic pills prescribed by our excellent physician. The physician also arranged for her to have an infusion of monoclonal antibodies which helped to increase her own creation of natural antibodies.

On January 6, in the morning before I was to take her for her antibody infusion treatment, I told her:

"You are on the way to recovery."

She just smiled for the first time in days, and it was like a smile from heaven for me.

"I know what I am talking about." I added.

I still did not tell her about my meditation action, thinking she would read about it anyway when she would be editing this book.

As a Reiki Master, Juanzetta, understanding the workings of healing energies and metaphysics, also took healings from her friends. An energy and metaphysical healer, Kim, gave her treatments in which she pulled the virus out of Juanzetta's cells, leaving the cells healthy. And another friend, Charles West, did a treatment reactivating

Juanzetta's healthy DNA from the time of her physical birth. After all these things, she started to gradually get better and gain back her normal vitality. When I was finishing these lines on January 14, 2021, she told me with a smile that she had just received the message that her second Covid19 test was negative.

I want to emphasize that alternative, especially metaphysical ways of treatment, will have a bigger effect on you if you genuinely believe in them yourself in the first place and have a positive approach to whatever you try. When you think outright that all of it is just quackery with misleading false promises, it probably will not work. Those of you who are of the Christian faith probably understand what I am talking about. Jesus, according to the Gospels, said numerous times that faith was what healed a person when he performed his famous miracles.

Chapter 60
DISCOVERY

"Tell people that there's an invisible man in the sky who created the universe, and the vast majority will believe you. Tell them the paint is wet, and they must touch it to be sure."
(George Carlin)

I used the Catapult again in early January 2021, about the same time when Juanzetta was fighting Covid19. I had a feeling that there was still something particularly important to be found in the high transitional and non-form dimensions of our Universe. I really did not know what I was seeking. I decided to use the same way as I had already travelled there several times. This time I did not have any specific intention. I decided to catapult myself into the 8th dimension, the middle transitional dimension, and just wait to see what could happen or what messages I would receive.

And, shockingly, an amazing discovery hit me, like lightning directly from the Source. I realized I was in Focus 80. The clear message came to my mind that these highest focus levels corresponded numerically to the highest transitional and non-form dimensions in our Universe.

Before I define these highest vibrational levels and describe them, I need to mention that whenever we travelled in the programs at The Monroe Institute into Focus 49, we were in the top vibrational layers of the 5th dimension of our Universe. We were fully aware of and utilizing form vehicles and form based non-verbal communication. We apparently unknowingly and sporadically also ventured into the last and vibrationally highest form-based 6th dimension, where Focus 60 is the top vibrational layer. The following is a description of other higher vibrations and dimensions:

Focus 70 is the top vibrational layer of the 7th dimension of our Universe, or the lower transitional dimension.

Focus 80 is the top vibrational layer of the 8th dimension of our Universe, or the middle transitional dimension.

Focus 90 is the top vibrational layer of the 9th dimension of our Universe, or the upper transitional dimension.

Focus 100 is the top vibrational layer of the 10th dimension of our Universe, or the lower non-form dimension.

Focus 110 is the top vibrational layer of the 11th dimension of our Universe, or the middle non-form dimension.

Focus 120 is the top vibrational layer of the 12th dimension of our Universe, or the upper non-form division, and where we can reach the Stargate.

Any metaphysical traveler can reach any other focus, like Focus 73, 97 or 114, in the same way. When more travelers reach a particular focus level, they make it easier for those who will follow in their footsteps to find it. It would be the same process as the already created structures like the TMI There in Focus 27, the Alpha Squared Station in Focus 42, or Alpha X in Focus 49. Their forms are very dense and stable because so many Monroe Institute students have visited and utilized them. Focus levels 98 to 105 have also stronger densities, because they are the vibrational frequencies utilized in the Starlines Reunion program for linking fragments of our consciousness. As such, they are used by the Starlines Reunion spiritual travelers whether consciously intentionally or subconsciously. The density and stability, however, are matters of our perception because they are in a non-form vibrational environment.

I was wondering why I did not discover all this earlier, since it seems now to be so clearly obvious. In addition, I also understand that the Catapult command consists of two parts, the word Catapult itself and the number of the focus level where I want to go. I intend to practice and use this for research in those dimensions later. And you, Dear Reader, can do that also, when you learn to understand the power of intention, as well as Love, gratitude, and determination as you endeavor to your own metaphysical journey.

Chapter 61
COINS, RACE AND TIES

"The very best proof that something can be done is that someone has already done it." (Bertrand Russell)

During my spiritual journey, I usually went into meditation with three intentions. Likewise, I reflected often on three dreams intuitively knowing they would be related. The dreams very often meant that I was contacted by my guides or star friends for another conversation. After I finished the draft script of this book in early February 2021 and gave it to Juanzetta for editing, I had three interesting dreams again.

I was collecting large golden coins, maybe 3 inches in diameter in the first dream. I had a full bag of them, and I was sure they were mine. However, I quickly realized that I would have to leave them at the place where I found them. The next day in a dream I was running in a race. I overtook the leading runner who was expected to win the race while we were on a wide road. I knew that a narrow mountainous path was coming soon. He was right behind me when we got to the narrow path, and he was breathing heavily on my neck, but he could not pass me. When we saw the finish line not far away, he tried forcefully to push me out of the way. I pushed him back and he failed to run through the small booth where the finish line was. I ran through the booth with both arms high over my head with a victory scream and woke up.

Three days later in a dream, I went to buy some ties in the Radio Shack store where I used to moonlight many years back. They recognized me and showed me their bottom drawer where the ties were held. I picked out a variety of different sizes and wanted to pay. They told me I could have those ties without paying.

It took me almost a month to have a successful meditation about the messages from those dreams. I used the Starlines Reunion CD for support, but I had already successfully trained me to bypass and ignore the guidance on the tape. I just amplify the Hemi Sync in the background. I usually take off on my own way after arriving at TMI There in Focus 27. I subconsciously knew I would have to use my new command and catapult myself out of there. I expressed the intention to use Catapult 120 and went directly in an instant into the 12th dimension of our Universe.

Michael and Robert were there already, but they had no forms or wings. Very gentle euphoric waves of knowing were loosely, slowly, and majestically flowing around me creating blissful feelings. I posed the question of whether they sent the dreams and why I had to come to Focus 120. They spoke to me as one and I immediately understood the unimportance of who was who. I had already learned a long time ago that there is no need to taint the messages with unimportant details.

"We had to intervene, Jozef and we needed you to come here. You finished your second book, and you need to do a self-evaluation from here, as you would say on the Earth, from above. You need to look at your spiritual accomplishments from here, from our and your Elohim angelic essence. You will understand what we mean when we explain the happenings from your dreams, which we sent to you."

"You were telling me that even if I would be able to accumulate some wealth like those golden coins, I could not take them with me here, weren't you?"

"That is right, Jozef. And nobody can, regardless of whether their names are Musk, Bezos, Branson, Bigelow, Gates or else. Those men are getting older and starting to understand that. They now are worrying not only about their money, but also about their final graduations from your planet not knowing what is next, or whether there is any next. We had to stop you, Jozef. You cannot compromise your spiritual and metaphysical achievements with money from someone else."

"What are you talking about, my Dearest Brothers?"

"About your planned entry into that Robert Bigelow contest

which is trying to prove by material means that we do exist here. Such a proof cannot be bought with money, Jozef. You do not belong in their company; let them seek their proof and see what they will get. You know better than that, Brother. The proof is inside of every human soul on the planet and cannot be taken out. Every human being has to find that proof inside of her or his own soul."

"That is exactly why I wanted to challenge the contest. Did you shut down the modem in our house when I wanted to send my application?"

"Yes, we did, indeed."

Now I must interrupt that conversation and explain the subject matter to you, Dear Reader. The famous aerospace entrepreneur Robert Bigelow founded the Bigelow Institute for Consciousness Studies in June 2020. The institute created a contest with financial rewards for 3 essay winners. The prizes are significant, $500 thousand, $300 thousand, and $150 thousand dollars. Participants had to first apply by documenting their ability to answer the question: "What is the best available evidence for the Survival of Human Consciousness after Permanent Bodily Death?"

I was ready to enter the contest, despite not seeing The Monroe Institute or The Michael Newton Institute named in the list of relevant institutions. I carefully filled out the application with Juanzetta's editing help and was ready to send it in well ahead of the deadline of February 28, 2021. Juanzetta and I were feeling good about it. When I wanted to click the button, the Internet connection suddenly was interrupted. I took the printout, and we looked at it again. Juanzetta read all lawyer jargon in it and simply asked me: "Are you sure you want to do this?"

And we suddenly understood that the modem failure was a divine intervention. We sat down to talk, and it was clear that I could possibly lose my author's freedom of publishing. I was not naïve enough to think that I could win any prize, I just wanted to challenge the paradigm of the contest.

And now, back to my conversation with Michael and

Robert in Focus 120. I told them:

"I understand and we are very thankful to you, Brothers. I did not want to enter the contest for money. I just wanted them to widen their approach. And I thought maybe I could get some more publicity about my spiritual research and books."

"You are lucky that you have Juanzetta, Jozef. We can tell you that. You could have screwed up big time!"

"What about my dream about the race, Brothers?"

"Despite your complex metaphysical and spiritual knowledge, Jozef, you are running on a very narrow path. Only a few can join you in your race and some might try to beat you in an unfair fashion. Even though you could lose that narrow race in your physical body, you are already a clear winner. Your narrow path here is clear for you after you expire in your physical body. Only a few can ascend here directly from their physical bodies."

"What do the ties represent? I asked.

"Those are your ties, your connections to those who understand your message. They were of different sizes in your dream. The ties can be short or long, tight, or loose, short term or long term, but they are always genuine. You can build or accept as many ties as you wish. Everyone taking an opportunity to create a tie with you can build upon your example. They can use your inspirations for their own way to journey back to their real true spiritual home according to their wishes and desires."

"Thank you, my Dear Brothers. Can I have another question?"

"You can have as many as you want, Jozef."

"Can I leave a visible material sign about my true essence on the Earth after I expire from my physical body?"

"You could possibly do that, but why would you want to do so, Jozef? Why would you give them a fish for free? Let them learn how to fish and then they can catch their own fish."

Chapter 62
SHIP AND TRAIN

"It's not what you take when you leave this world behind you, it's what you leave behind when you go." (From the song Three Wooden Crosses by Randy Travis, Songwriters Kim Williams, and Doug Johnson)

The earthly local time had gone by, and it was August 21, a very important date in the calendar for me. The Warsaw Pact armies invaded Czechoslovakia on that day in 1968, I married my second wife Sasha in 1986 in Austria, and I applied from New York in 1988 for work as a radio journalist at the Voice of America in Washington DC. And now, in 2021, my sons had suggested we celebrate a Name Day for Juanzetta on this date. It was her first Name Day ever. Also, a good day to start to add one more chapter to this book. Just another wonderful synchronicity. Earlier, because Juanzetta and I had gotten fully vaccinated in April and May 2021, we were able to spend eight wonderful days on our beloved Viking ship Orion at and around lovely Bermuda in July.

The script of this book was generally finished in early March of 2021. However, I continued in my internal struggle of whether to publish it at all. Again, I am a very happy man living in a wonderful loving relationship with my Juanzetta. Despite that, I am continuing to have apocalyptic dreams about the end of our civilization and the world as we know it. These include a lot of violence in the streets of not only people against each other, but also personally against me. I am often accused of a capital crime I did not commit or sometimes beaten to death by a mob. It does not make any sense to me. And I hope that I am not correct about my feelings that the dreams might be about happenings yet to come. However, I do not want to go into any concrete prophetic predictions here, and I never will.

Today, society in our country and worldwide is almost hopelessly divided along ideological, religious, race, ethnic and even sexual orientation lines. Instead of focusing on how we should reasonably relate to each other, we are overemphasizing our own identities and putting labels on others around us. The labels are very often based on shallow cliches. Then, we demand that the others should live according to our very specific wishes. Yes, the problem is not who we are, but how we treat each other, often without respect and dignity which can lead to terrifying consequences.

The amazing advances in information technology, the Internet, tremendous databases, and our smartphones unfortunately have also brought unexpected problems. Our individual meanings and freedoms are rapidly fading away with benefits remaining mainly for corporate elites and those in the government holding vast powers as never before. The social media are being utilized as vehicles for often unjustified attacks, threats, and intimidations against fellow human beings.

We are literally being domesticated and farmed for the prosperity and lavishness of a few. Greed is on the march. While the idea of globalization seems to be meant well by its proponents, the main building blocks of civilization from the past which were based on a common language, border and culture are disappearing. Fences, according to the adage, are supposed to make good neighbors who admire and respect each other. But fences are not desired by those who want to control everything from the top. They need ruthless equalization achieved by killing opportunities for everyone on the planet, except for themselves and their closed circles. The tremendous diversity and variety unique to our planet is slowly but surely disappearing. We are voluntarily enslaving ourselves more and more without most people even realizing it, seemingly being happy by thinking that they are getting a little bigger piece of the pie than the others. The most productive are happy slaves enthusiastically watching each other.

These were the ponderings fueling my reluctance to

publishing this book. I was also quite busy with preparing some necessary paperwork, like my will, advance health directive and instructions for my family in the case I would unexpectedly die. There was, however, the feeling somewhere in the back of my mind that there was something that still needed to be added to the script in case I would decide to publish it. Not much, maybe only a symbolic closure or just a final paragraph. I went through my diaries from March to August looking for help. I found three interesting dreams:

On March 20, I was dreaming about getting ready to go with two astronauts on a ship deep into space to look for proof of the existence of God. They chose me to go with them because I was a spiritual expert. However, I was a little reluctant and afraid, almost sure that we would never come back to the Earth.

In my second dream in the early morning of April 28, I was again dreaming about the end of the world. Five of us, four old men and one old woman, were in a building waiting for the end. We decided to kill ourselves together. Someone cooked a poisonous stew, and the woman gave a plate of it to each of us. I faked it and did not eat it. I did not want to die, but the others were on to me. I ran into the attic, and they followed me. When I opened the door to the roof, tremendous heat forced us to go back. I realized that the other members of the group had not eaten the poison either. I screamed at them and said:

"Nobody can go out. We must try to survive here. Let's go to look for some good food and establish some order. We have to elect our leader!" And I woke up.

In the early morning of July 31, I had a dream of being on a big ship where everything was tip-top, and it was a wonderful sunny day with a nice calming breeze. But, as we were going into our cabins for the night, the captain warned everybody:

"It is going to be bad; we will be attacked, and everyone will need to find shelter and protection on your own."

Then the attacks started coming from all directions. Explosions were everywhere, broken pieces of equipment and body parts were bursting into the air and falling into the water all around the ship. But the ship itself seemed to be indestructible and it continued its sailing as if nothing was really happening. The morning came and all was quiet again. Those of us who had survived the night started cleaning. With surprising enthusiasm, we were throwing away not just the debris from the deck, but a lot of junk we had accumulated in our cabins. Everyone who survived was happy to be alive and ready to continue our cruising on a clean and revitalized ship with newfound energy.

I set up the intention for my meditation about those three dreams. I decided to visit Michael and Robert in the highest non-form 12th dimension of our Universe. I wanted to ask them about looking for God by utilizing cosmic travels and if they had any messages for us about a possible catastrophic, apocalyptic end of our civilization and the destiny of our physical Earth. I suspected that the ship in my dream represented our Earth, our giant ship cruising throughout our vast Universe. I hoped to use the information they would give me for my earlier mentioned desired closing of this second narrative of mine.

I expected to resolve it in one meditation; that was a mistake indeed. I had not been meditating for quite a while and the difference between the frequency of my current vibrations and vibrations of the 12th dimension was much bigger than I thought. I had to build up my ability steadily with a total of five meditations.

In the first one, I directly catapulted myself into Focus 120. The awareness of gentle homogenous waves appeared; likewise, I was aware of the Ultimate Membrane. I also received the message:

"You are now surrounded by Elohim Waves."

I sent the signal calling for both Michael and Robert. I knew they were there for sure. But the fact of having not meditated for a long time and tiring my physical body out with all kinds of exercises and other activities meant that I clicked out and fell asleep. I was awakened a few seconds before the end of the CD with the expulsion of a bunch of roses from my crown chakra, accompanied with a short and loud female moaning shout. I knew my effort was recognized.

The next time, I expressed my Catapult 120 command more decisively and the awareness of the Elohim Waves was clearer. When calling on Michael and Robert, I first received the message from them that I should not think about the forms and shapes of energy vehicles I used to get there, to the Elohim Field, as they said. I heard that name for the first time and understood that we all three were present in the Elohim Field. They wanted me to be fully free and separated from forms and shapes. They also wanted me to understand the difference between the new way of communication in the Elohim Waves environment and the utilization of ROTE communication of which I was so comfortable using. Then, suddenly my physical body was happy again to have some deserved rest, and I clicked out and fell asleep.

In my third meditation when I became aware of the Elohim Waves, I detected two slight additional superimposed movements of waves in an otherwise completely homogenous Elohim Field. I knew those were caused by Robert and Michael reacting to my presence and my desire to communicate. I sent out the question about my first dream regarding travelling with two astronauts and looking for God. They answered:

"Astronauts will not find and cannot find God for anybody from their physical ships. That was why you were reluctant to go with them. Astronauts can only find other physical objects and civilizations. And those physical civilizations are eons away. Yet everyone looking for the true God can follow your example and come here to touch and kiss the Ultimate membrane, the Skin of God. Anyone coming here can also find their Stargate, peek in it or even disappear into it."

Then I quickly clicked out again.

In the fourth meditation I combined the catapult

technique and light body missile. I got into the Elohim Field quickly, but almost immediately went into click out barely thinking:

"I guess there will again be no answers today."

Finally, remembering that the best time for meditation is in the early morning after only a few hours of sleep, I did just that at 2:40 am. I combined the energies of catapult, slingshot, and light body missile methods. After   instantly getting into the Elohim Field, I sent an inquiry about my two other dreams. Here is what I received from Michael and Robert:

"Dear Jozef, first we have to emphasize that you and every human being on the planet is dying alone, no matter how many people are around in the time of the final departure from the human body. Of course, you can hold the hand of your dearest Juanzetta, and she can hold yours. But you sail to the other side alone in the moment of death. You can eventually reconnect with her and anybody else who has departed before you. You can also connect instantly with the higher beings who reside there. If you would find yourself in an apocalyptic situation, you should plan for a smooth transition while you are still in your physical body. If you cannot physically help anybody around you, get away from the crowds to avoid accidental death, especially when there is unmitigated panic and hysteria around you. We suggest that you avoid committing suicide even in such a situation unless you would be in unbearable physical pain. You need to prepare yourself for a smooth graduation by leaving your physical body consciously with full control of the process of your departure, like when you were dying as Menev centuries ago in Rhaeto Romansh Switzerland. That way you can help your loved ones by gathering them after they have also departed and give them proper instruction of how and where to go according to their wishes. Finally, you should stick to your plan for the afterlife that you created with your deep spiritual studies while you were alive in your physical body."

"Thank you so much, Dear Brothers. What did the dream

about the ship mean?"

"The ship in the dream was your planet Earth indeed. There are millions and billions of such ships in the manifested universes. Your ship is quite unique. You as a spiritual being are also unique even though you are connected to the One. Do not worry about your ship. The Earth has survived shake-ups many times before and she will continue her cruising with you or without you. There are enough ships in the manifested universes for every soul wishing to reincarnate, even if they cannot return to Earth. You should not leave Earth when she is troubled and you are not dead yet, even if it means that many people would perish. When you survive an apocalypse, help to clean your ship of all unnecessary garbage and revitalize it like you did with the ship in your dream."

"What can we do to prevent any upcoming catastrophe? When could it happen?"

"We cannot give you any date, any way or the scale of destruction. We do not know either. But we can give you hope and advice. The hope that people on the planet will start to treat each other without prejudice, greed and hate, but rather with respect, compassion and mutual understanding and cooperation so catastrophes can be avoided. Everybody should start reforming themselves through revitalized spirituality as you suggest in your books. Reform yourself first without seeking to reform others."

While I was working on this chapter, I received another dream reflecting my worries, but also giving me big hope even without my asking for interpretation. I was riding in a train full of people. I was thinking that it was going too fast. Suddenly the brakes were squealing, and the train hastily and heavily stopped. Some passengers around me slid off their seats. I looked out from the window. The track in the front of the locomotive was just on the edge of a giant gorge without any bottom to be seen. If the train had continued recklessly at the same speed and had not stopped, it would have fallen into the abyss, and we would all die.

In the dream about the ship, the disaster happened. But, in the train dream, the disaster was averted. Therefore, as Michael and Robert told me, we citizens of Earth need to work on reforming ourselves through revitalized spirituality and, thereby, help to avoid the disaster.

EPILOGUE

"The history of science tells us that the future students of nature will laugh at our conservatism and lack of vision."
(William Corliss)

One of the reviewers whom I met personally during one of my early presentations of *How to Kiss the Universe* wrote that the book was a "Not quite a how to..." I cannot argue with him and, of course, I value his willingness to write a review for such an obscure book from an unknown author from a faraway land. I have had the guts to write and publish a non-fiction book in English, despite English not being my mother tongue and that I speak with a Central European accent. I learned the hard way that a segment of the population in our wonderful United States of America still has prejudices about people who speak in accented English. That is happening even though many people who wanted to get here and love the country often speak several languages. The most prejudiced ones are usually those who speak only English and often only in their local vernacular.

Even the title of my first book begins with "How to...," it is the personal story of a reporter who was awarded the rare Gold Medal from the Voice of America for delivering the news to listeners in a meaningful way and entertaining fashion. The stories presented in both books were gained by direct experiences. I clearly understand that they might be only New Age beliefs or even hallucinations for you. Only if you are willing to step out of your human shell and find out for yourself, as the great Robert Monroe was always saying, can you learn how to kiss the universe and experience the afterlife beyond the limits of the universe. You can do that only when you understand that you are an unlimited, timeless, multi-dimensional and unconditionally loved spiritual being, part of the integrated Oneness of metaphysical reality.

Likewise, *Toward the Ultimate Source* is also a "not

quite how to...." Nobody can tell you exactly how. The universe is vast, as some spiritual explorers say. It does not have boundaries, as others say. What I am telling you, Dear Sister or Brother, is that the manifested environment of the bubbles of the universes is infinite and our Earth is just a piece of dust in another bigger piece of dust, the bubble of our universe. That is what our Universe truly is. Our understanding of everything is merely a matter of observing perceptions by our senses and beyond our senses. You should be open to that perception and then you can sit on the bubble of the universe as an angel, or even travel inside into your own cells. When you leave your human shell forever, your perception by senses will be gone. You must be ready for your new perception. And that is also what my books are about. Perhaps, as the greatest remote viewer Joe McMoneagle once said:
"If I cease to exist, the whole Universe will not exist as well."

It is also especially important to understand that there is a divine order existing, which was created for spiritual beings to have physical experiences. The manifested physical environment, including our planet, was created as a school with a dual nature. One's physical life can continue only by the constant killing of other lives, regardless of whether those lives are bacteria, plants, or animals. All living beings have their place in the reality manifested by the Ultimate Creator and are fulfilling their purpose by their living and dying.

For those of you who are vegan, do you really think that plants are not aware of dying and suffering when they must? You must understand that plants, and even bacteria and viruses, have consciousness. Do not think that lions will stop eating meat and start eating grass. I also need to say something to the blind light workers and worshippers. Planets will continue to absorb meteorites and galaxies will continue to eat and absorb galaxies. Stars shall continue dying to give a place to new celestial bodies and yes, to a new light. That is their purpose.

You may not know your "how to" after you read my books, but you can get tremendously inspired to discover your individual true origin, essence, and destiny. To get where I am now, i.e., spiritually free with only the necessary physical and spiritual ties to my Totality of Self or to the Chunk of the Infinite Sea of Bonded I-There Clusters is not easy. It is a long, long spiritual journey with hard work, impossible without understanding and building up and practicing unconditional Love. Unconditional Love is needed to reach the velocity for leaving the Earth Life System. Then you can continue to try to reach the Ultimate Choice. Finally, you can have an option to leave the whole manifested spiritual reality or to become an angel again and reside in the place of unconditional Love.

There are infinite numbers of these places of unconditional Love vibrationally existing close to the Ultimate Creator. Juanzetta and I call them Ramas. Only those spiritual beings who have experienced everything necessary to understand the Ultimate Freedom and have produced enough Super-Loosh have the right to approach the Ultimate Choice, which is total unity with God. The Source of Everything continues in the manifestation of energy and matter, and likewise in annihilating them. Striving to understand why God's creations which are made from pure unconditional Love become compromised in a manifested environment is an everlasting reason for continuing to study.

If you decide to go on a spiritual journey to be free of the fear of dying and the afterlife, you can continue to grow step by step. Your guides and other spiritual leaders whom you may not know yet will clearly let you know that. You can likely find, however, that the ultimate spiritual reality is something completely different for you than for me. Then you can debunk me, and I will be happy that you found your own way to the truth.

The Covid19 scares with all the shutdowns designed to exercise unheard of control over all of us should be a reminder for everyone. Science fiction books often write and warn about civilizations' self-destructions. Because I love this wonderful planet and all of you people regardless of what gender, race, nationality, language, political affiliation, sexual preferences and religious beliefs or non-beliefs you are, I wrote my books. I hate no one. Juanzetta and I know what to do and where we go after we die. I hope that you will figure it out for yourself, too, without anyone else conditioning and manipulating you to their advantage, whether in the physical environment here on the Earth or after your departure into the afterlife.

ABOUT ME AND BOOKS

"Home is not where you were born; it is where you choose to die." (The mother of the poet Richard Blanco stated on the Diane Rehm Show on New Year's Day of 2014).

I was born in a small village called Láb in the western part of current Slovakia shortly after the communist putsch in Prague had established a totalitarian regime in Czechoslovakia. Our region is called Záhorie, which I would translate as the land behind the mountains. It is inhabited by idiosyncratic people who are often the subject of jokes for the rest of the country. But they do not mind it and they are very friendly and warm.

Our family struggled under the communist regime because my dad was a social democratic dreamer who refused to succumb to the Communist party bosses. He was thrown out of the Communist party when it swallowed the Social Democrats under a unified totalitarian umbrella. Yet he continued to dream all the time. My beloved mom determinedly kept me and my four siblings alive, but I often went to sleep hungry.

Our human spirits were frozen by the communist regime. I was being told in the school that there was no God; at home, my mom was reminding me to go to the church in the village. The unknown grandma in one of the favorite jokes being told in by Communist governed Czechoslovakia says to her grandson:
"Janko, quickly pray. Meanwhile I shall iron your Red Pioneer scarf."
This was the kind of environment we were living in. But my dad's dreamer genes were very much alive in me and, even as a child, somehow, I knew that one day I would need to leave that troubled country.

The Communist regime tried to suppress any flow of free information with an iron fist. Living behind the Iron Curtain made us hungry for any open or hidden messages from the outside world. I always tried to see our mailman first to get the four-page newspapers ahead of my Dad. When he was the first approaching the mailman, then I tried to pull the newspaper from his hands. Our miniature elementary school library was created by one of the enthusiast teachers trying to help the kids. I always impatiently yearned to read and understand whatever book they had. We had only two books at home, *Far away from Moscow* and *The Golden Book of Slovakia*. The first time we had a radio in our house was when I was fourteen years old. At that time, a television was just a distant dream.

Yet, despite growing up as a poor village boy, I managed to go through college and go on to earn the equivalent of a master's degree in Broadcasting Technology at the Slovak Technical University. Then, I became the Chief of the Department in the computer center of the National Broadcasting Technology Company of Slovakia. Later, I also earned a postgraduate degree in computer systems programming at the Czech Technical University in Prague.

But my heart was always somewhere else. I dreamed constantly of becoming a writer. I was fascinated with science fiction, the only genre which was able to escape the watchful eyes of the Communist censors just a little bit. The urge to write never left my heart, although I did not really know what my message was supposed to be.

Then after several years of listening to The Voice of America in my living room in Bratislava, I decided to leave my motherland. The dream of working for that organization became a driving force for what I believed was my life mission. I could not breathe under the Communist regime. I decided to try to reach the United States and help the people of Czechoslovakia become free with my work at the VOA.

The first unsuccessful attempt to escape through Yugoslavia happened in the summer of 1984. In 1986, under even more dangerous circumstances, I finally reached Austria with my family. The door to freedom had opened. We got to America in 1987. In 1993, I became a United States citizen and learned to love my newly adopted motherland, although I continued to love my dear Slovakia as well.

I became an American in every true sense. I even learned to understand and love baseball. Earlier in my life, I wanted to know why the Frenchmen Louis Pauwels and Jacques Bergier, in their magnificent work *The Morning of the Magicians,* had written that on the other side of the Atlantic a new society had been born. I wanted to know why the USA was leading the world. Today, after living here all these many years, I understand why she is often called the last hope for humanity. She is truly a place where hopes and dreams can live and come to fruition. I also hope deep in my heart that she will get out of the current crisis and be healthy again.

More than twelve years of radio journalistic work at the Voice of America are now behind me. When the Slovak Service was closed after the communist regime fell, I moved into the engineering aspect of the VOA and continued to work there until retirement in October 2015.

As Americans, we carry boundless hope in our hearts that we can preserve our society and way of life. We hope, as only Americans can do, that our fast-moving train will not crash even though, at the end of the tracks, there may be nothing but an abyss.

In the year of 2008, I began to understand that my life mission on this planet was more than just working for The Voice of America. I realized that I had to write a book about my spiritual experiences as I was often reminded by my spiritual friends to do so. You are now holding one of my books in your hands or reading it online. I hope that you enjoyed it and that it gave you a lot to think about.

When I was growing up in the totalitarian Czechoslovakia, it was not easy to find good books that were not tainted by the official repressive policies of a communist regime. One little exception in my former country and in the Soviet Union and its other satellites was science fiction. It sneaked into our minds with its brave concepts and stories right under the noses of the government censors. They let it go, apparently, because the books for them were just fantasies and not threatening the regime. We learned to read a lot between the lines and then applaud under the table and keep it to ourselves. I can just mention Arkadij and Boris Strugackij or Alexander Beljajev from the Soviet Union, the Czechs Karel Čapek and Jaroslav Veis, my teacher from elementary school in Slovakia Alta Vášová, and the great Stanislaw Lem of Poland. I have widely read also western science fiction, some of the books while still in my former motherland and a lot of them here. I was also able to read the samizdat literature smuggled to Czechoslovakia from abroad, and I could read some works of authors like George Orwell and Alexander Solzhenitsyn.

Later, after coming to the United States, I especially liked all kinds of serious apocalyptic books and movies pondering about what we would do if we were really facing a global catastrophe and our total elimination. A few of those you might know, Dear Reader, are *Armageddon, Deep Impact, Independence Day, 2012, The Road, Children of Men, On the Beach and Book of Eli.* There are many excellent others, of course. I also have had and am still having many apocalyptic dreams. My Juanzetta, who does not like these types of movies at all, started to say while we were watching the newscasts about the Covid19:
"Gosh, this is just like Science Fiction!

Yes, the virus experience was like science fiction, my Dear Friend! I knew for about nine years before the corona virus that something awful would happen in the second half of April 2020. I had had a series of premonitions and precognitions throughout the years. I just did not know if it would be about all of us or just about me. In the past, I predicted the breakup of the Soviet Union, Czechoslovakia, Yugoslavia, and the first war in the Persian Gulf (in that one case literally the exact hour). Of course, I was laughed at and ridiculed by my friends and colleagues.

We are fragile, scared, and afraid human beings,

even when we do not have to be. My dear friend Peter sometimes sarcastically says:

"Aren't we shaking, being terribly afraid to lose our chickenish lives?"

I am always telling him that I am not, and he does not believe me, because to shake about our chickenish lives according to Peter is normal. I am not shaking because my body and my circumstances would be different than yours, my friend. I am not shaking because I am aware of the true spiritual reality, and I have experienced it many times. I am not shaking because I have also been here on this planet many times, have seen it all and do not need and do not want to come back, even though I like sex, booze and fried chicken and love my children. I also know where I can go after I die. There are a lot of choices for you my friend, too. I have just narrowed them for myself, so I will not have to wander around for a long time and look for help in the vastness of the afterlife.

ACKNOWLEDGEMENTS

I foremost must thank to my beloved wonderful wife Dr. Juanzetta Flowers. This second book of mine, My Love, would not be possible without your constant encouragement, continual advice, spirited conversations, and complete understanding. I thank you for the diligent and precise editing of the script, suggestions for improvement, and for correcting my English and grammar. Your unconditional love is unwavering, and I love you so much!

This book is the result of a loving husband and wife cooperation. We intentionally bypassed all the stages and people usually associated with classical publishing. We did not have time for that. Juanzetta always calls our books our babies. And we still can take care of our babies.

Then I must thank to Aldren Gamalo for his amazing cover artwork. Also, thanks go to the artist Rastan for the Angel Shaped Nebula used for the cover.

I would also like to express my profound gratitude to the kind souls who wrote supportive reviews of my first book *How to Kiss the Universe*. I have no idea who some of these souls are, but their support has been essential. My appreciation goes to Art H. and his first review of my book which made me cry, to William Buhlman, Isabella Johnson, Lee Hunt, Richard Natali, Glenn W. Hollis, Mike A., Subtle Traveler, Reviewer -S., India E., Alex, Mary from Illinois, Charles West, Pete Partin, B. Moss and Milan with his wife from Bratislava, Slovakia. Thanks to Patty Ray Avalon for her encouraging comment on You Tube. And a big thanks to Donald Lord for his comments on Twitter and You Tube. I also thank all of those who rated the book whether they liked it or not and those few who wrote rather the critical reviews.

And you, Dear Reader, can help us, if you wish to, to spread the message. It is fully up to you. Regardless of whether you do something or not, we are very thankful to you and hope that it has helped you in your life.

CONTACT:

howtokisstheuniverse.org

howtokisstheuniverse.com

jozefsimkovic.com

akopobozkatvesmir.com

jsimkovic@howtokisstheuniverse.org

howtokisstheuniverse@outlook.com

UPDATED METAPHYSICAL GLOSSARY

ACCESS CHANNEL (FOCUS 11):   vibrational level influencing a physical body directly from an altered state

AFFIRMATION: verbally expressed determination to achieve an altered state of mind and effectively execute a meditative intention

AKASHIC RECORDS (LIBRARY): records of all that has happened, is happening and will happen in a manifested universe

ALPHA SQUARED: an inter-stellar non-physical space station used by The Monroe Institute's spiritual explorers in Focus 42

ALPHA X STATION: an inter-galactic spiritual station with a Light Spa and a Subatomic Particle Accelerator in Focus 49

ALTERED STATE OF MIND: a state when a human mind is communicating more with a spiritual environment beyond the physical body than with the physical body itself

AMBASSADOR OF LOVE: angelic highest non-form spiritual being who decided to live as a highly skilled spiritual teacher in the environment of unconditional Love

ANALYTIC OVERLAY: recognized subjective speculative information during remote viewing or altered state

APERTURE: an opening leading into the Stargate and the unlimited consciousness and stillness of God

ASCENSION: the direct rapid vibrational move of a human soul from a physical body all the way toward the Ultimate Source

ASTRAL BODY: part of your consciousness which is not present in your physical body, but still having a form like your physical body

ASTRAL PROJECTION: when you successfully direct your consciousness to be mostly out of your physical body in the astral plane

ATLANTIS: the former island empire on Earth now in a non-physical realm where many of its suddenly departed post-catastrophic inhabitants live in a non-physical copy of their former environment

AVATARS: very highly developed spiritual beings who are helping humans to speed up their spiritual progress

AYAHUASCA: a soul wine used by shamans and their students for trips into an altered state

BASIC LAW OF SEPARATION: a principle defining the essence of manifested universes being separated from the uniqueness of God

BELIEF SYSTEM TERRITORIES: a complex variety of vibrational spaces where the souls of physically dead people reside and are under the influence of other spiritual beings

BERSERKERS: the elite group of Viking warriors who often went into a battle while in a trance

BIG ANNIHILATION: when a universe is sucked back into the stillness of the Source and completely disappears

BIG BANG: creation of a new bubble of a new universe by the intention of the Ultimate Creator

BIG CRASH: the opposite of the Big Bang, when a universe massively shrinks into the process of annihilation

BIMINI ROAD: the sequence of rectangular stones in the bottom of the sea near the Bimini islands of the Bahamas

BINAURAL MUSIC (BEATS): an alternative acoustic way of stimulating the brain which is used to induce an altered state of mind

BLACK HOLE: a gateway into different galaxies, clusters or even into different universes

BONDED I-THERE CLUSTERS: interconnected I-There clusters (Higher Selves) of spiritual beings incarnated in or attracted to planetary systems, galaxies, or local universes

BUBBLES: universes with local space and time created by God

BUBBLING: the process of God's expression from stillness into motion and manifestation

BUFFERS: storages of information during the process of the transferring of parallel spiritual realm batches into serial interpretation for your brain

CANALING: communication by humans with spiritual

beings through pathways created by the humans as opposed to channeling, which is when channels are discovered and not created by humans

CHAKRAS: energetic centers in the human body which enable the exchange of energy and information with nonphysical spiritual realms

CHUNK OF INFINITE SEA OF BONDED I-THERE CLUSTERS: when you have collected all your experiences and remaining Loosh and integrated your spiritual structure into a point in front of the Stargate

CHEC UNIT: Controlled Holistic Environmental Chamber at The Monroe Institute which provides isolation from light and outside sounds

CLUSTER COUNCIL: a governing body composed of high spiritual beings who are guarding the balance and development of spirituality for inhabitants incarnated in the cluster of galaxies

CODE OF MANIFESTATION: the code similar to DNA in biological bodies on Earth that is enabling the manifestation into a different space and time

CONSCIOUSNESS (also MIND): our spiritual essence, different and separate from matter and energy, but which enables us to manipulate them using the power of intention

CONSCIOUSNESS ONE (C 1): when your earthly mind is mostly present in your physical body in the first three dimensions

COSMIC LOVE: unconditional Love supplied by the Ultimate Creator which is expected to be cherished, magnified and returned to God from all manifested living beings

COUNCIL OF GALACTIC GUARDIANS: the governing body composed of high spiritual beings guarding the balance and development of spirituality of inhabitants incarnated in a galaxy

COUNCIL OF STARS FRIENDS: the group of high spiritual beings helping the author of this book in his spiritual journey, chaired by Gardener

CREATORS: highly developed spiritual beings close to God who can manifest planetary systems and conduct terraforming

DARK ENERGY: the global balancer and the global glue between the bubbles of universes

DARK MATTER: the local cosmic balancer and glue inside the bubble of a universe

DEMONS: spiritual beings who have lost their silver cord connections to God

DERVISH: a member of the Sufi order who is using energetic whirling dancing for bringing his consciousness into an altered state

DEVIL: a malicious powerful spiritual being without a connection to God

DIMENSION: a distinct spiritual vibrational space between membranes separating it from lower vibrational space and from a higher vibrational space

DIVINE STRUCTURE OF CONSCIOUSNESS: a hierarchical tree-like structure of interconnected spiritual beings maintaining their connections to God

DNA: a molecule that carries the genetic instructions used in the growth, development, functioning and reproduction of all known living organisms

DOPPELGANGER: an apparition or double of a living person

EARTH LIFE SYSTEM (ELS): the physical and spiritual space where the Soul is significantly more bound to our physical plane than to a wider spiritual reality

ELOHIM: the highest spiritual beings who are close to God from shortly after separation from the Source or before the final return to the Source

ELOHIM FIELD: formless environment close to the Source where the highest non-form spiritual beings reside

ELOHIM WAVES: spiritual activity of the highest non-form spiritual beings detectable and recognizable by spiritual travelers from Earth

EMOTIONAL CLEANSING: the process of removing

unwanted conditions from your mind before you can effectively utilize an altered state

EMPTINESS (AETHER): a meaningless void perceived by the meditating mind as a blackness

ENERGY CONVERSION BOX: a storage for a variety of subjects and influences which could disrupt your meditation

EVER PULSATING NOW: the process of expanding and shrinking local bubbles of universes in no time

EXPECTATION: a wished for but usually not guaranteed result of your meditation

EXPLORATION 27: the program at The Monroe Institute dedicated to the study of the vibrational level of the higher astral plane of Focus 27, where the Park is also located

EXTRA SENSORY PERCEPTION (ESP): the ability to perceive information in other ways than just by the five senses

FACILITATOR (TRAINER): a certified teacher and spiritual helper at The Monroe Institute

FALLEN ANGELS: unfriendly spiritual entities who have lost their connection to the Ultimate Creator

FINGER OF GOD: the acknowledgment of connection and recognition from the Ultimate Creator when a new human being is conceived

FIRST TIMERS: spiritual beings who have finished their first earthly incarnations

FLATLAND: a two-dimensional universe, according to the fictional book by Edwin A. Abbott

FLOW: the stream of information while meditating when a canal is created

FLYING GRIZZLY: the author's first spiritual guide who appeared in that form

FLYING POTATO: a local transfer vehicle seen in Atlantis

FOCUS LEVEL: a loosely specified spiritual vibrational area of the mind in an altered state according to the model developed by Robert Monroe

FOCUS 10: when your body sleeps, but your mind is awake and alert, and you have reached a basic altered state of mind

FOCUS 11 (ACCESS CHANNEL): the vibrational level influencing a physical body directly from the altered state

FOCUS 12: when your awareness in an altered state widens beyond the five senses and enables you to communicate with non-physical realms

FOCUS 15: an altered state of mind with no time perception

FOCUS 18: an altered state of mind for exploring unconditional Love and emotions

FOCUS 21: an altered state of mind bridging physical and non-physical realms

FOCUS 22: a spiritual vibrational space where the souls of people still living on Earth can temporarily pop-up from their physical bodies for a variety of reasons

FOCUS 23: the lower astral plane, a very dense spiritual vibrational ring around our planet where most of the recently departed souls of physically dead people reside

FOCUS 24: the lower vibrational space of the Belief System Territories where less developed souls with a strong affinity for very manipulative collective belief systems reside

FOCUS 25: the middle vibrational space of the Belief System Territories where souls with an affinity for mainstream religious and ideological systems reside

FOCUS 26: the higher vibrational space of the Belief System Territories where souls with a loose affinity for like-minded non-religious or non-ideological communities reside

FOCUS 27 (also the PARK): the spiritual vibrational space inhabited by souls who have overcome the lures of the lower vibrational levels and are getting ready for further conscious development in the Earth Life System

FOCUS 34/35: the spiritual vibrational spaces immediately beyond the Earth Life System; a platform for starting voyages beyond the planet and deep into the galaxy and beyond; also, the gathering place

FOCUS 42: the spiritual vibrational space well beyond the Earth Life System, yet still local in a planetary and galactic sense

FOCUS 49: the inter-galactic spiritual vibrational space, yet still local to our Universe

FOCUS 60: the top vibrational layer of the 6th and last form-based dimension in our Universe

FOCUS 70: the top vibrational layer of the 7th and lower transitional dimension in our Universe

FOCUS 80: the top vibrational layer of the 8th and middle transitional dimension in our Universe

FOCUS 90: the top vibrational layer of the 9th and upper transitional dimension in our Universe

FOCUSES 98 to 105: the vibrational frequencies from the Starlines Reunion program for linking fragments of our consciousness

FOCUS 100: the top vibrational layer of the 10th dimension of our Universe, or lower non-form dimension.

FOCUS 110: the top vibrational layer of the 11th dimension of our Universe, middle non-form division, enabling inter-bubble travel

FOCUS 120: the top vibrational layer of the 12th and highest non-form dimension, the front of the Stargate, close to the Skin of God

FOCUS 130: the 13th dimension inside of God, beyond any manifested bubble of the universe, it is the unity with the Ultimate Source

FOX DEN: the community room in the Nancy Penn Center of The Monroe Institute for socializing and sideline discussions

FRONT LOADING: staining the mind with speculative or wishful information ahead of a remote viewing or spiritual travel

GAIA (MOTHER GAIA): our planet Earth as a living organism

GALACTIC CORE: the center of the galaxy with a gateway into another galaxy or universe

GANESHA: the Hindu god with an elephant head, a big belly and four hands, the Lord of success and the destroyer of evils and obstacles

GATEWAY VOYAGE: the first fundamental life changing

meditative program at The Monroe Institute

GARDENER (MICHAEL): the angelic Milky Way's administrator of Loosh and the author's main spiritual teacher

GENERATORS OF MANIFESTATION: spiritual devices producing a strong force for pushing intention into energy and matter

GENERATORS OF RELEASE: spiritual devices producing a weak force for releasing experiences and Loosh into consciousness

GESTALT: a received and constructed skeleton of a target in remote viewing

GHOSTS: the souls of departed people residing in a lower astral plane and, occasionally, slightly, and temporarily manifesting in the physical

GOD (SOURCE): the formless, timeless, and unlimited power of creation, the unlimited sea of interconnected consciousness

GRADUATE: a spiritual being who has finished the process of reincarnation and education on a planet

GRATITUDE: the appreciation and thanks for information received from non-physical realms

GREAT EMITTER: the source of universal unconditional Love beyond the Stargate, outside of the manifested universes

GROUNDING: the process of calming down and bringing your vibrations back from a spiritual activity into the physical environment

GUARDIANS: the higher spiritual beings securing the safety of our planet and her purpose as intended by the Ultimate Creator and the Creators

GUIDE (also GUARDIAN ANGEL): a spiritual entity always willing to help you in an altered state and in your physical life

GUIDELINES: The Monroe Institute's program focusing on the development of relations between you and your inner self

HADIEN: the author's spiritual star friend from a different

galaxy who appears in a pyramidal form

HEARTGATE: an oversized activated heart chakra receiving Love directly from God

HEARTLINE: the program at The Monroe Institute dedicated to the spiritual study of the human heart and emotions

HEMI SYNC: the patented Monroe Institute's audio technology which produces different tonal sounds into your left and right earphones to achieve an altered state of mind

HIGHER SELF (I-THERE CLUSTER): the part of your consciousness residing permanently outside of your body, vibrationally hovering over the planet and always willing to help you in your physical and spiritual journey

HIGHER-HIGHER SELF: the consciousness of a spiritual being containing multiple higher selves

HYPNAGOGIC STATE: the borderline between the asleep and awaken state

IMMORTALITY: the essence of all spiritual beings who are mostly not aware of it

INFINITE SEA OF BONDED I-THERE CLUSTERS: all loosely interconnected Bonded I-There Clusters

INTENTION: the driving force of creation and a tool for manifestation and manipulation

INTER-DIMENSIONAL GENERATOR: a metaphysical device for generating the energy needed to enable crossing a dimensional membrane

INTERFACE: a part of the third eye enabling communication with the spiritual world

INTERGALACTIC COUNCIL: a governing body composed of high spiritual beings who oversee big areas of the Universe

INTERNAL SELF HELPER (ISH): your personified internal power and guide always willing to help you when you ask

I-THERE CLUSTER: the hovering Higher Self of a spiritual being incarnated on a planet

KAHUNA: a Hawaiian wise man, wise woman, or Shaman

KAMALÁSKA: the author's Internal Self Helper in female form, who is more than a friend but less than a lover

KARMA: an account of your actions, including previous lives, influencing your current life and expressing your spiritual value

KUNDALINI: a hidden energy sleeping at the base of the spine, coiled like a snake waiting to be unleashed

KUNDALINI LOOP: the continuous flow of godly energy from the Source and back through all human chakras in both directions

KUNDALINI MACHINE: a spiritual device in the Park for helping souls who are recovering from earthly traumas to instantly connect to their Higher Selves

LAST TIMERS: spiritual beings planning to leave the Earth Life System permanently after they have finished their education on Earth during their last reincarnation

LAW OF KARMA: the universal principle of raising or lowering your spiritual value in harmony with Love or in contradiction with Love

LEMURIANS: the inhabitants of a former continental empire on Earth

LIFELINE: the program at The Monroe Institute dedicated to helping the souls departed from Earth by spiritual explorers who are still living on the planet

LIGHT BODY: the highest vibrational energy body fully transformed into the form of light with the help of a Subatomic Particle Accelerator

LIGHT SPA: a chamber enabling transformation from a high vibrational energy body into a light body

LINELAND: a universe with only one physical dimension, as described in the book *Flatland* written by *Edwin A. Abbott*

LOCAL KARMA: your spiritual value in the effort to become a Graduate and reach the velocity needed to be able permanently leave a planet

LOOP OF CREATION: the flow of the creative intentions of God into the manifested universes and back

LOOP OF LOVE: the flow of Love from the Source through

your Heartgate and then back to the Ultimate Creator

LOOP OF SOULS: the intertwining bond between soulmates enabling them to repeatedly incarnate together

LOOSH: a non-form substance flowing to God that is created by the emotions and experiences of all sentient living beings

LUCID DREAMING: when you know in a dream that you are dreaming

LUCIFER: a malicious powerful spiritual being who voluntarily severed his connection to God

MACHO: a spiritual being called on by the author with the intention to suppress his own ego

MANIFESTATION: the process of creating or affecting a physical or other form-based reality by using the power of the mind

MC SQUARED: The Monroe Institute's program dedicated to confidence building and psychokinetic practices

MEDIUM: a person with abilities to see the past, present, and future events of another person by tuning into the spirit energy surrounding that person

MEMBRANE: the distinct borderline between the two distinct levels of spiritual reality and dimensions

MEMORY ROOM: a non-physical chamber for explorers containing the tools and devices for enabling communication with the Akashic Library

MENEV: the author's most important reincarnation on planet Earth as a folk healer in Rhaeto Romansh Switzerland

MICHAEL (GARDENER): The Milky Way's angelic administrator of Loosh and the author's main spiritual teacher

MICRO-WORLD: the manifested physical reality we discover when our mind is moving more and more inside elementary particles and their components

MIND (CONSCIOUSNESS): our spiritual essence distinct and separated from matter and energy; it enables us to manipulate them

MIND OF THE BODY EXPERIENCE: when you know that most of your earthly mind is out of your physical body

MIRANON COLORS: a set of channeled colors helping the imagination to rise through the vibrations from Focus 15 to Focus 21

MISTER Q: a higher spiritual being with interest in the origins of planets and living biological beings

MIZU NO KOKORO: a Japanese expression for a peaceful mind being like calm water without any disruptions

MONARCH: the governor of the one-dimensional universe described in the book *Flatland* written by *Edwin A. Abbott*

MONKEY MIND: a natural state of mind in the awake state with scattered random thoughts of all kinds

MONROE INSTITUTE: a non-profit organization in Virginia dedicated to the study and research of human consciousness

MONROE PLANETARY UNIVERSITY OF CONSCIOUSNESS: the future name and mission of the current Monroe Institute in the late second half of the 21st century

MONROE PROTOCOL: one of the reliable ways to get to an altered state

MORPHON: a spiritual official in the Recovery Center in the Park who is assisting spiritual explorers when they carry out Soul retrievals

MORPHOGENETIC FIELD: the field of thoughts created by everything in existence

MULTI-DIMENSIONAL: being able to operate simultaneously in different dimensions of the universe or universes

MULTI-EYES: the spiritual tools for simultaneous seeing into many different dimensions and universes

MULTI-TELEPORTER: a spiritual device enabling advanced high beings to do simultaneous teleportation into multiple spaces and times

MULTIVERSES: multiple overlapping bubbles of universes

NON-FORM BEINGS: highly developed spiritual beings free of the need to have any shape or form to be aware of their essence and actions

NON-VERBAL COMMUNICATION: the exchange of information between spiritual beings in a no time environment, usually by exchanging balls of information

NOW: the ever-present moment with time not having any dimension or locality

ONENESS: all spiritual beings interconnected with the Source and between themselves

ORBS: beings from metaphysical dimensions manifested on our physical planet as small slowly moving lights

OTHER SIDE: the expression commonly used for the non-physical reality of a spiritual realm

OUT OF BODY EXPERIENCE: when you are aware of your non-physical body being temporarily separated from your physical body

OVERSEER (JESUS or JESHUA): the highest known spiritual being very close to God, highly respected and admired by anyone whom the author met during spiritual travels

PALENQUE: the Maya city state in southern Mexico that flourished in the 7th century

PARALLEL UNIVERSE: the overlapping space and time with a different bubble of a created universe

PARK: a spiritual vibrational space for the conscious recovery of souls from the traumas of physical reincarnations and for planning their further spiritual development

PERSONAL CLUSTER COUNCIL: a temporarily created ad hoc body of higher spiritual beings for helping any spiritual being who ask for it

PLAUTUS: the Roman comedy playwright and the author's third most important reincarnation on planet Earth

POINT: a universe without physical dimension

POINTLAND: a universe without physical dimension as described in the book *Flatland* written by *Edwin A. Abbott*

PORTAL ROOM: a non-physical chamber enabling teleporting into a different space and time

POWER OF ONE: power of consciousness superior to Many

PROTECTIVE ENERGY BALLOON: a protective energy

barrier around your spiritual body form when travelling in an altered state

PSYCHIC: a person using extrasensory perception (ESP) to identify and process information hidden from the five known human senses

PSYCHOKINESIS: the ability to move physical objects on Earth with the power of the mind

PULSARS: very dense cosmic objects used by super-intelligences for identifying and correcting dangerous imbalances in the physical universe

PURE THOUGHT: a source for the creation of a thought with a shape, form, and intention

QILIN: a mythical hooved chimerical creature known in Chinese and other East Asian cultures

QUANTUM ENTANGLEMENT: the technology used by high spiritual beings to create the Code of Manifestation for teleportation and manifestation into a different space and time

QUANTUM UNIT: the smallest amount of any physical entity involved in an interaction

RA: one of the spiritual beings who is enforcing the divine order in the Universe

RAMA: a spiritual home between bubbles of universes composed of unconditional Love where angelic beings reside

RECOVERY CENTER: a place in the Park, where many souls departed from the Earth recover from their planetary traumas

REINCARNATION: when your Soul is embodied again in physical form for another physical life

REMEMBER: a command in an altered state for helping to remember an experience

REMOTE VIEWING (PERCEPTION): a psychic ability driven by protocol enabling one to successfully describe remote objects, persons, environments, and happenings

REPEATERS: spiritual beings who repeatedly reincarnate on Earth

REPTILIANS: unfriendly spiritual entities who lost their

connections to the Ultimate Creator

RESIDUAL CONSCIOUSNESS: a part of the mind remaining in the physical body during an out of body, near death or altered state experience

RESONANT TUNING: the process of aligning your vibrations with a variety of the frequencies of the Universe

RESONATOR: a spiritual tool for aligning with the Universal Harmonic Frequency of the Universe

RETRIEVAL: a process of helping stuck souls to move on to a higher vibrational space by spiritual explorers still physically alive on Earth

ROTE (RELATED ORGANIZED THOUGHT ENERGY): a ball of information exchanged between communicating higher spiritual beings

ROTER: a spiritual explorer routinely communicating with higher realms using ROTEs (balls of information)

ROTING: creating, exchanging, and processing ROTEs (balls of information)

RUALA: the higher spiritual being appearing in the female form helping the author to understand the feminine part of his essence and Cosmic Love

SATAN: a malicious powerful spiritual being without a connection to God

SCHOOL OF CREATORS: a gathering spiritual place for the Creators (Elohim) who are close to God

SCREEN OF MANIFESTATION: a tool for the unwinding of a ROTE

SHADOWS: substances created when consciousness starts to manifest or when matter and energy start dispersing into the consciousness

SHAMAN: a traditional intermediary between physical and spiritual worlds

SHAMAN'S HEART: a former program at The Monroe Institute dedicated to the blending of traditional shamanic practices with Hemi Sync technology

SILVANA: a planet for processing Loosh in our galaxy

SILVER CORD: a connection (pointer) between the physical

and astral body and between spiritual bodies on different vibrational levels

SINGULARITY TRANSFER POINT: a spiritual point through which consciousness from our time and space can immediately move to any other time and any other space

SKIN OF GOD: the Ultimate Membrane separating the Source from the manifested universes

SKJOERG: the author's second most important reincarnation on planet Earth as a Viking shaman

SLINGSHOT: a spiritual technique for a rapid increase in vibrations by using the combined spiritual energy of a group of explorers and the Earth Core energy

SOUL: the organized consciousness of a timeless and multi-dimensional spiritual individual

SOUL STRETCHING: when consciousness anchored in the physical body is projected and stretched to an intended target

SOUL TRADERS: malevolent spiritual beings offering deceiving deals to human souls residing in the Belief System Territories

SOURCE (GOD): the formless, timeless, and unlimited power of creation, a borderless sea of interconnected and universal consciousness

SPECIAL PLACE: a non-physical place created by The Monroe Institute student for use when she or he wants to meet with spiritual guides

SPIRITUAL BELT (RING): a spiritual space around our planet where the souls of the departed reside while still overwhelmingly bound to the Earth's physical environment

SPIRITUAL HYBRID TRAVEL TECHNOLOGY: travel using consciousness stretching, carrying information needed for manifestation and then materialization of a physical body at the destination

SPIRITUAL INTEGRITY: when your goals and actions are the same in your physical awareness, dreams and altered state

SPIRITUAL CHILDREN: thought forms in the spiritual realm created by the fantasies of lovers

SQUARE: a main character as described in the book

Flatland written by *Edwin A. Abbott*

STARGATE: a gateway, portal out of the stars and out of the manifested universes into the infinity of the spiritual Source

STARLINES: The Monroe Institute's program dedicated to communication with spiritual entities beyond the Earth Life System

STARLINES II: The Monroe Institute's program dedicated to communication with galactic and inter-galactic spiritual entities

STARLINES REUNION: The Monroe Institute's program dedicated to initiating physical contacts with extra-terrestrials and extra-dimensionals

STARMAN: the author's spiritual star friend who has experiences from reincarnations on the Earth

STRINGS: elementary units of manifestation created immediately after a Big Bang which rapidly multiply like viruses or bacteria

STRONG FORCE: a force produced in generators of manifestation which pushes the flow of intention from consciousness into matter

SUBATOMIC PARTICLE ACCELERATOR: a spiritual device in the Light Spa for helping a high energy vibrational body to be transformed into a Light Body

SUPER-LOOSH: a purified high quality Loosh, Super-Love, giving the Ultimate Creator a reason to manifest more Big Bangs and Universes

TELEPORTER: a spiritual device in the Memory Room enabling the mind's projection into a different space and time

TERRAFORMING: a process executed by the Creators for preparing a planet for the introduction of sentient biological beings

THOUGHT FORMS: energy forms in the spiritual realm created by human minds

THREE SISTERS: a sea rock formation near the Bimini islands in the Bahamas

TIME BALL: a spiritual tool enabling access and shortcuts into the past and future across the bubbles of universes

TIMELINE: a program at The Monroe Institute dedicated to the study of time and its influences on people

TIME WHEEL: a spiritual tool enabling access and shortcuts into the past and future in a local universe

TMI-THERE: a non-physical copy of The Monroe Institute in the Park

TOTAL KARMA: the sum of the karma accumulated from all your I-There Clusters in your effort to become an Ultimate Graduate and reach the Stargate

TOTALITY OF SELF: when you have collected all your experiences and remaining Loosh and integrated your spiritual structure into the point in front of the Stargate

TRUE HEAVEN: unity with God, the Ultimate creator

ULTIMATE CHOICE: the choice of a spiritual being who as an Ultimate Graduate can decide whether to return to God or stay in the place of unconditional Love as a skilled spiritual leader and teacher

ULTIMATE CONCEPTION: when a spiritual being is born by separation from the Source

ULTIMATE CREATOR: God, Source, timeless and borderless consciousness

ULTIMATE GRADUATE: a spiritual being who has reached the state where he or she has learned everything that was possible in the manifested universes

ULTIMATE HIGHER SELF: the complete consciousness of a unique spiritual individual having only one unique silver cord connection to God

UNIVERSE: a local space and time bubble with a defined number of dimensions and flexible boundaries manifested by the power of the Ultimate Creator

VIBRATIONAL LEVEL: a quantified specific frequency of a spiritual energy body oscillation

VIMANA: an intercontinental Atlantean aircraft

VORTEX: an energy form of a spiritual being forced into spinning by intention

VOYAGER 8: an inter-dimensional spacecraft used by the three Starlines programs participants for spiritual travels

WEAK FORCE: the force produced in generators of release which pushes Loosh from matter into consciousness

WORMHOLE: a spiritual tunnel beyond space and time connecting two different black holes in different galaxies and universes